PRIMARY PARTNERS

A-Z Activities
to Make Learning Fun

for Ages 8-11
Old Testament

47 Activities that Coordinate with the *Primary 5* Manual with Matching Thought Treats and Scripture Challenge Cards

Use for Primary Lessons, Family Home Evening, and Daily Devotionals to Reinforce Gospel Topics

You'll Find: A-Z Topics to Match Primary Lessons #1-47

Atonement   Attitude   Choose the Right   Christmas
Commandments   Covenants   Creation   Eternal Life
Example   Faith   Fasting   Forgiveness   Friendship   Happiness
Heavenly Father's Plan   Holy Ghost   Honesty   Humility
Jesus Christ   Love   Mission   Obedience   Peer Pressure
Prayer   Preparing   Priesthood   Prophet   Repentance
Sabbath Day   Sacrifice   Scriptures   Second Coming
Temple Marriage   Testimony   Tithing   Trust
Wisdom   Word of Wisdom   Worship   Zion

Covenant Communications, Inc.
American Fork, Utah

Printed in the United States of America
First Printing: January 1998
Second Printing: December 2001

Primary Partners: Old Testament—Ages 8-11

Covenant Communications, Inc.
ISBN 1-57734-264-X

Mary H. Ross, Author and
Jennette Guymon-King, Illustrator
are the creators of

PRIMARY PARTNERS BOOKS & CD-ROMS

Lesson Match Activities and More:
Nursery and Age 3 (Sunbeams) Vol. 1 + CD-ROM
Nursery and Age 3 (Sunbeams) Vol. 2 + CD-ROM
CTR A Ages 4-7 + CD-ROM (color)
CTR B Ages 4-7 + CD-ROM
Book of Mormon Ages 8-11 + CD-ROM
Old Testament Ages 8-11 + CD-ROM (color)
New Testament Ages 8-11 + CD-ROM (color)
Doctrine and Covenants Ages 8-11 + CD-ROM (color)
Achievement Days, Girls Ages 8-11 + CD-ROM
Quick-and-Easy Achievement Days Ages 8-11 + CD-ROM (color)
Primary Partners: Clip-Art on CD-ROM (500 images-color)
Singing Fun! (each year's theme) + CD-ROM (color)
Sharing Time (each year's theme) + CD-ROM (color)
Sharing Time TEACHING TOOLS (each year's theme) + CD-ROM (color)

FAMILY HOME EVENING BOOKS & CD-ROMS:

File Folder Family Home Evenings + CD-ROM
Home-spun Fun Family Home Evenings 1 + CD-ROM
Home-spun Fun Family Home Evenings 2 + CD-ROM

YOUNG WOMEN BOOKS & CD-ROMS:

Young Women Fun-tastic! Activities Manual 3 + CD-ROM (color)
Young Women Fun-tastic! Activities Manual 1 + CD-ROM
Young Women Fun-tastic! Activities Manual 2 + CD-ROM (color)

MARY H. ROSS, Author
Mary Ross (shown below) is an energetic mother and has been a Primary teacher and Achievement Days leader. She loves to help children and young women have a good time while they learn. She has studied acting, modeling, and voice. Her varied interests include writing, creating activities and children's parties, and cooking. Mary and her husband, Paul, live with their daughter, Jennifer, in Sandy, Utah.

JENNETTE GUYMON-KING, Illustrator
Jennette Guymon-King (shown above) has studied graphic arts and illustration at Utah Valley State College and the University of Utah. She served a mission in Japan. Jennette enjoys sports, reading, cooking, art, gardening, and freelance illustrating. Jennette and her husband, Clayton, live in Riverton, Utah. They are the proud parents of their daughter, Kayla Mae, and sons, Levi and Carson.

INTRODUCTION

PRIMARY PARTNERS:

Lessons #1-47 Activities to Make Learning Fun

Old Testament

for Primary 6* Ages 8-11

Primary teachers and parents, you'll enjoy using the PRIMARY PARTNERS activities to supplement your Primary lessons, enhance family home evenings, and help children learn gospel principles in fun, challenging ways. Children love these easy, fun-to-create visuals. Patterns for each project are actual size, ready to Copy-n-Create in minutes to make learning fun. Don't miss the Gospel Standards activity for lesson #47 (pgs. 90-91).

TO MAKE IT EASIER TO COLOR OR COPY IMAGES you will also find this book on CD-ROM to print images instantly from your home computer in full color or black and white. Just ask for the *Primary Partners Old Testament* CD-ROM (shown right).

How to Use This Book

1. **Use the Lesson #1-47 Table of Contents** to match your lessons found in the Primary 5* manual.
2. **Preview A-Z Table of Contents** for visuals to match your gospel subject.
3. **Copy Patterns Several Weeks Ahead.** You'll save time and avoid last-minute preparations.
4. **Shop Ahead for Simple Supplies.** Activities require a few basic items: Copies of patterns, scissors, light/pastel markers or crayons, tape, glue, zip-close plastic bags, paper punch, yarn or ribbon, metal brads (paper fasteners), and pencils.
5. **Organize Activities** 1-47 for Primary lessons or A-Z for family home evening and Sharing Time.

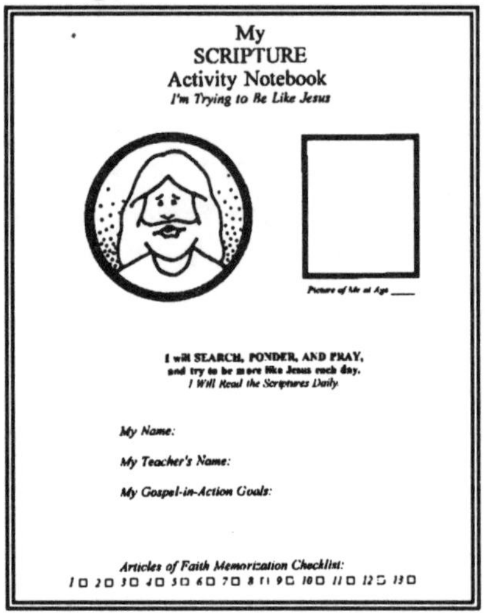

6. **Activity Journal:** Provide each child with a 3-ring binder or folder to store classroom creations in. Encourage children to display activities in their room before placing them in their notebook. Place the "I'm Trying to Be Like Jesus" cover page (shown left, following this page) in notebook with the child's picture next to Jesus. Children can fill in their personal goals and information.
7. **Scripture Challenge Cards:** You'll find Scripture Challenge Cards in numerical order #1-47 to match lessons #1-47*.

TO US SCRIPTURE CHALLENGE CARDS:

Step #1: Challenge Scripture Reading. Assign a SCRIPTURE CHALLENGE CARD each week (see patterns, pp. 92-116). Children can read the scriptures assigned and fill in the blanks on the featured scripture.

Step #2: Reward for Scripture Reading. As children bring the completed card the next week, reward them with a large glue-on sticker to match the image on the card. This larger sticker shows children that their testimony grows as they read the scriptures.

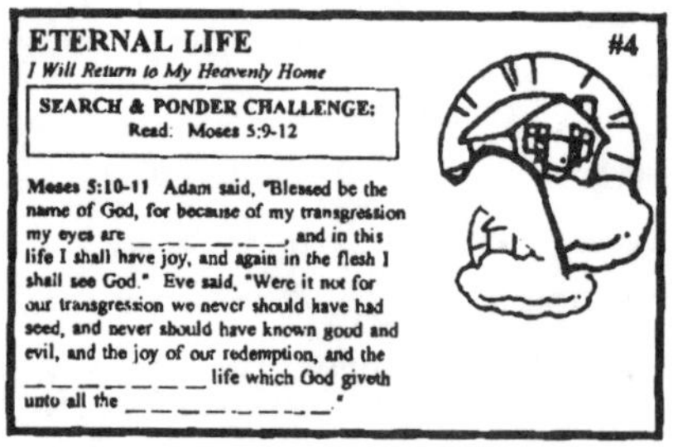

Step #3: Help Children Organize Cards. Option #1: Punch holes in card tabs to create a book; use rings or lace together (see book cover label, p. 92). Option #2: Store cards in a zip-close plastic bag (cut off left tab). Place label in front of cards.

*Primary 5 manual is published by The Church of Jesus Christ of Latter-day Saints, Salt Lake City, Utah.

My SCRIPTURE Activity Notebook

I'm Trying to Be Like Jesus

Picture of Me at Age ____

I will SEARCH, PONDER, AND PRAY,
and try to be more like Jesus each day.
I Will Read the Scriptures Daily.

My Name:
My Teacher's Name:

My Gospel-in-Action Goals:

ARTICLES OF FAITH Memorization Checklist:

1 □ 2 □ 3 □ 4 □ 5 □ 6 □ 7 □ 8 □ 9 □ 10 □ 11 □ 12 □ 13 □

Lessons #1-47 Table of Contents

* *Primary 6* manual is published by The Church of Jesus Christ of Latter-day Saints, Salt Lake City, Utah.

 A-Z CONTENTS

ATONEMENT
of
Jesus
Christ
SOAP

"And we know that all things work together for good to them that love God."
If life gives me lemons... I'll make lemonade!
I can go the second mile today to live the gospel of Jesus Christ.

Jacob
Esau

LOOK AHEAD

MIND POWER
I can keep my thoughts clean and pure.

StarBright
That Special Night!
Jesus

Love God
No graven images
No swearing
Keep the Sabbath holy
Obey parents
Do not kill
Be chaste
Do not steal
Do not lie
Do not envy
The 10 Commandments
light up my life!
Obeying the Commandments can be a piece of cake, simple as 1,2,3!
1. Read the scriptures 2. Pray 3. Listen to the Holy Spirit to guide me.

FOLLOW
RIGHTEOUS
LEADERS
TRUST
AND TELL GAME

SWIM
SINK
SINK

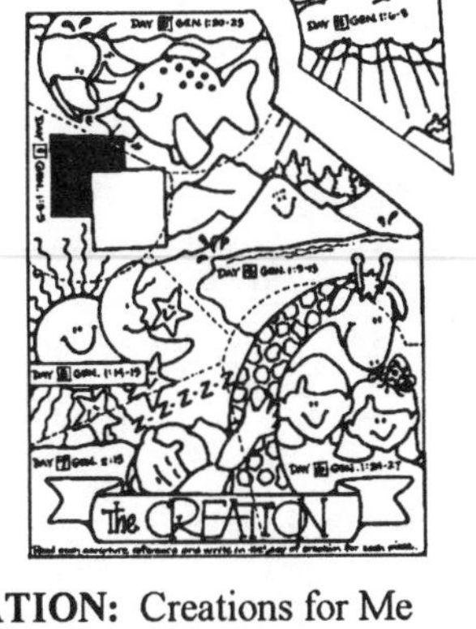
The CREATION

I CAN RETURN MAZE
Because of
Adam and Eve
Because of
Jesus Christ

I will follow in the footsteps of Jesus Christ
I will endure to the end as I...
Faithful Footsteps Flip
Pray to Heavenly Father
Pay my tithing
Attend church
Read the scriptures
Choose the Right

PORTRAIT OF MY SPIRITUAL HERO
TRAITS TO FOLLOW:

Trials make me strong so I can return to my Heavenly Father. Trials are necessary to make me strong, just as the tiny bird must work his way out of his shell. Trials give me strength!
D&C 136: 31

Fasting & Prayer Blessings

When I do FORGIVE I feel.....
peaceful
happy
loving
friendly
When I do not FORGIVE I feel.....
angry
jealous
unhappy
critical

Tell something about yourself so others may know more about you!
Tell someone in the circle something you know and like about

I choose to follow Jesus.
My Decision To Follow Jesus Reward List
We are miserable.
Our faith increases.
The Holy Ghost stays around us.
We are blessed spiritually.
We can resist temptation.
We are happy.
We lose our faith.
The Holy Ghost will not guide us.
We lose our spiritual blessings.
It is harder for us to resist temptation.

The Plan of Salvation
Premortal Life
Celestial Kingdom
Spirit World
Birth
Death
Resurrection
Final Judgment
Terrestrial Kingdom
Earth
Telestial Kingdom

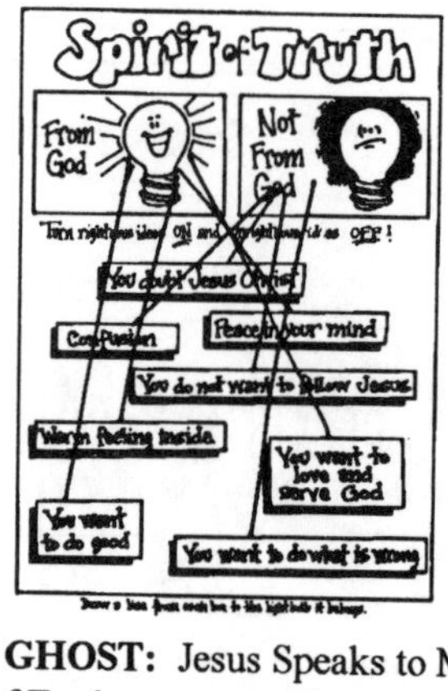
Spirit of Truth
From God
Not From God
You doubt Jesus Christ
Compassion
Peace in your mind
You do not want to follow Jesus
Warm feeling inside
You want to love and serve God
You want to do good
You want to do what is wrong

HONESTY PAYS!
Start
STOP
BUCK
BACK 2
MOVE 2
MOVE 3

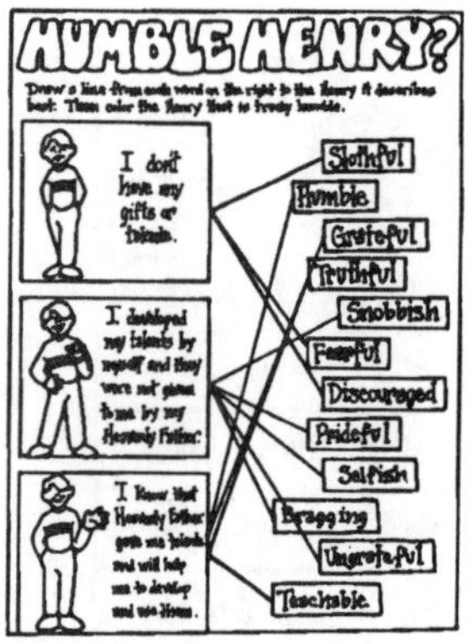
HUMBLE HENRY?
Slothful
Humble
Grateful
Truthful
Snobbish
Fearful
Discouraged
Prideful
Selfish
Bragging
Ungrateful
Teachable

Obey the Word of Wisdom
Love others
Others will love you
Tell a lie
Others will not trust you

My circle of LOVE
Spin & Serve Game
Shy Child
Troublemaker
Family Member
New Child
Older Neighbor
Visitor
Lonely Relative

A - Z CONTENTS

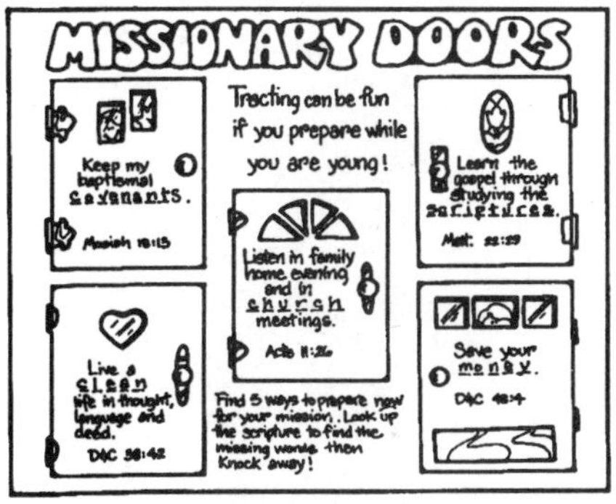
MISSIONARY DOORS
Tracting can be fun if you prepare while you are young!
Find 5 ways to prepare now for your mission. Look up the scripture to find the missing words then Knock away!

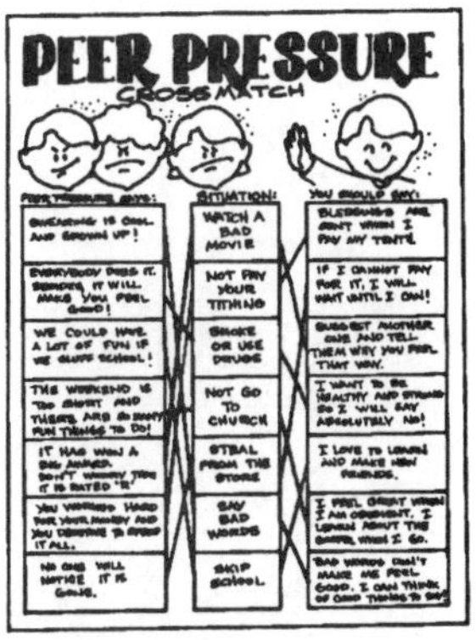
PEER PRESSURE
CROSS MATCH

MY PERSONAL GOLIATHS
Problems I can solve with the help of my Heavenly Father through prayer:

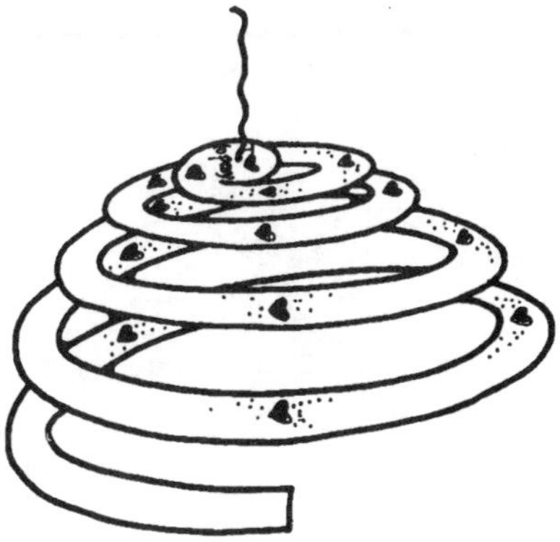

DOING NOW
DO IN THE FUTURE

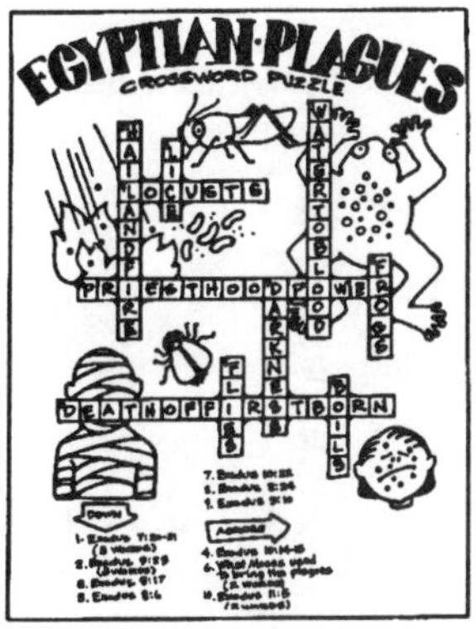
EGYPTIAN PLAGUES
CROSSWORD PUZZLE

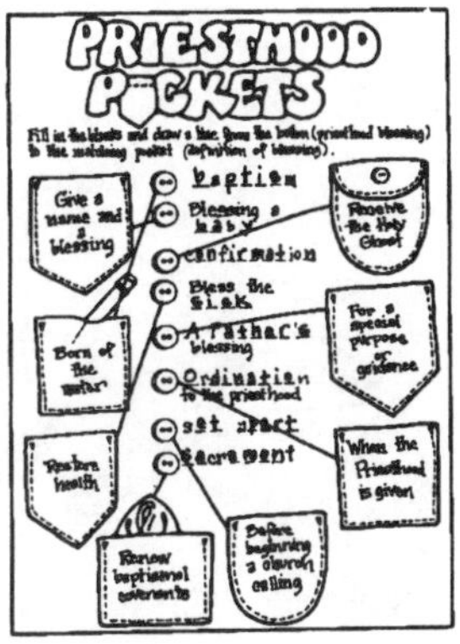
PRIESTHOOD POCKETS

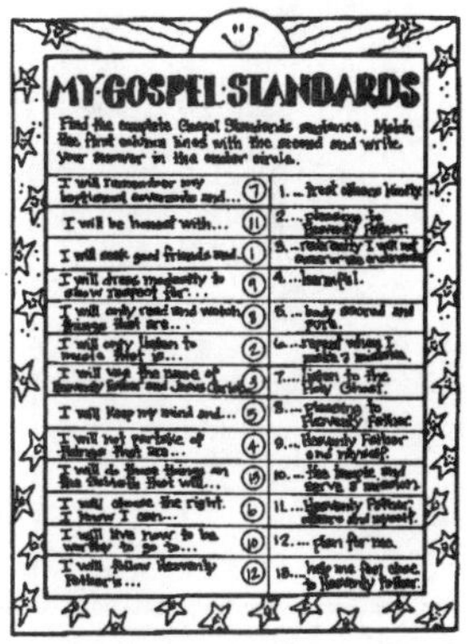
MY GOSPEL STANDARDS

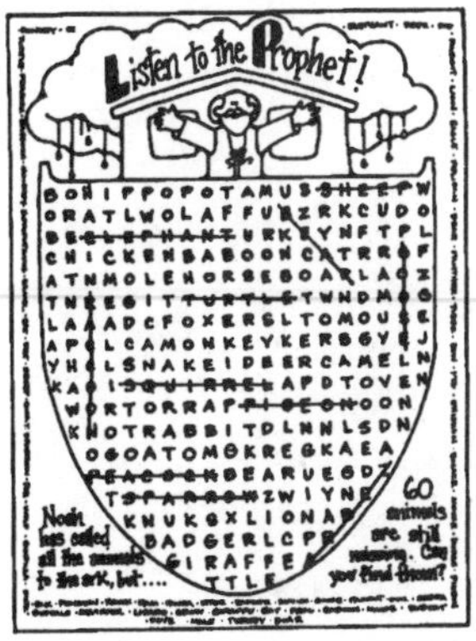
Listen to the Prophet!
Noah has called all the animals to the ark, but . . .
60 animals are still missing. Can you find them?

BITE SIZE MEMORIZE
Abide ye in the liberty wherewith ye are made free; entangle not yourselves in sin, but let your hands be clean, until the Lord comes.
D&C 88:86
What can I do to untie the ropes of wrongdoings?
(See D&C 58:42-43)

SABBATH DAY
ACTIVITY ADVENT CALENDAR
14 days 14 ways
to keep the Sabbath Day holy!

Tic-Tac-Toe
Do You Know?

Scripture Blessings
Sticker Challenge
Sunday
Monday
Tuesday
Wednesday
Thursday
Friday
Saturday

Millennium Match

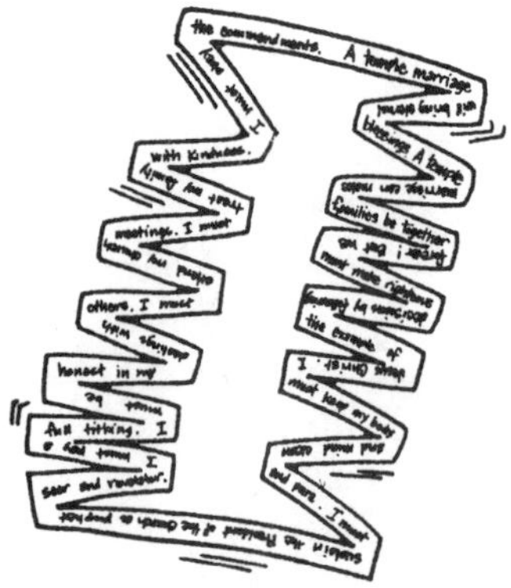

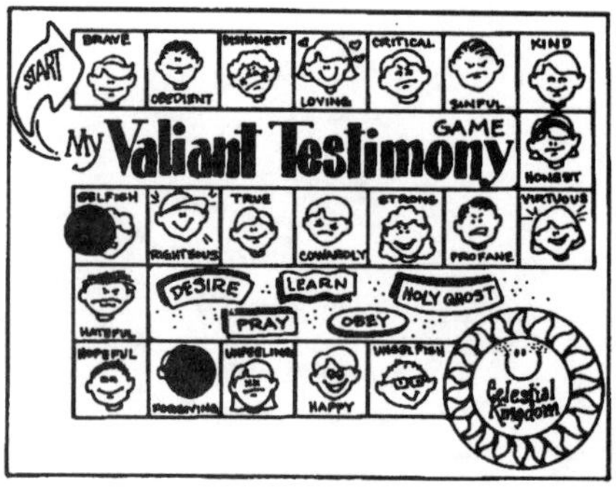
START
My Valiant Testimony GAME
DESIRE
LEARN
HOLY GHOST
PRAY
OBEY
Celestial Kingdom

Pending Spending
I must wait to spend my cash until my tithings paid; It makes "cents" for me to give and show I have obeyed.

BITE SIZE MEMORIZE
Trust in the Lord with all thine heart; and lean not unto thine own understanding. In all ways acknowledge him, and he shall direct thy paths.
Proverbs 3:5-6

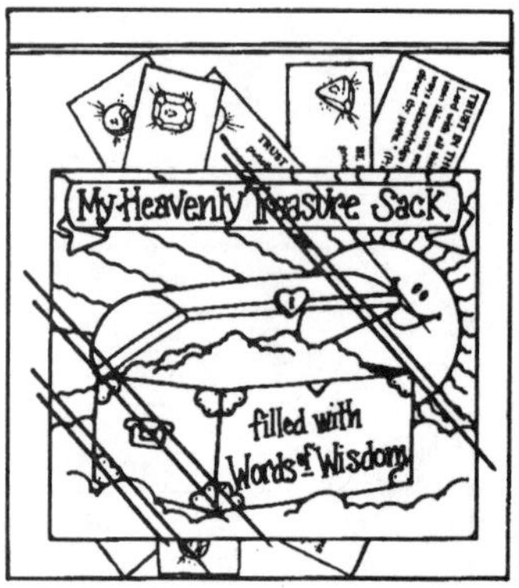
My Heavenly Treasure Sack
filled with Words of Wisdom

Word of Wisdom
Choices
MATCH PUZZLE

I HONOR HEAVENLY FATHER, JESUS AND THE HOLY GHOST
Worship WORDFIND

I LOVE
ZION
PURE IN HEART GAME

*Lesson #1**

HEAVENLY FATHER'S PLAN Is For Me

(Plan of Salvation story board and quiz)

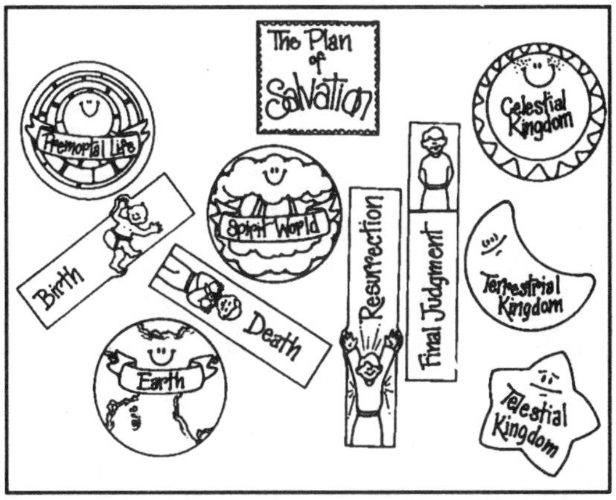

YOU'LL NEED: Copy of Scripture Challenge card (pages 92-93), salvation story board figures and wordstrips (pages 2-3) on cardstock paper for each child. Copy pages 2-3 in the Primary 6* manual (discussion and questions) for each child. Provide scissors and crayons.

Review Enrichment Activities #3, #5, and #6 (page 4) in Primary 6 Old Testament manual.*

ACTIVITIES:

IDEA #1: Create a Plan of Salvation Story Board. (1) Color and cut out salvation story board figures. (2) Place figures on the wall with tape as you discuss the questions on page 2-3 in the manual*. Children can take home to share with family and friends.

IDEA #2: Premortal Life and Earth Life Quiz. (1) Place quiz wordstrips (e.g. "Life with Heavenly Father and Jesus") face down. (2) Children can draw a quiz wordstrip and place it on the story board under premortal life, earth or both. Answers: Live with Heavenly Father and Jesus Christ (premortal), Be with our family (both), Have the Bible and Book of Mormon to guide us (earth), Have only a spirit body (premortal), Have a physical body (earth), Be taught Heavenly Father's plan (both), Experience hard work, sorrow, and death (earth), and Be able to have children (earth). Encourage children to present quiz to family and friends.

SCRIPTURE CHALLENGE: Do activity in class or at home.

THOUGHT TREAT: Celestial Smile Cookies. Add yellow food coloring to cookie dough before adding flour. Mix and roll into 2" balls. Press flat. Clip edges 1/4" inch with scissors or cut into with a knife to look like sun rays. Bake cookies. Frost center of cookie with yellow frosting (add 2-3 drops of yellow food coloring to vanilla frosting). Use candies to create a smiling face. Ask children to put on their celestial kingdom smile as they eat, imagining they are there living with Heavenly Father again.

*Lesson #2**

JESUS CHRIST Was Chosen to Be My Savior

(Choices & Consequences match game)

Review Enrichment Activity #2 (page 7) in Primary 6 Old Testament manual.*

YOU'LL NEED: Copy of Scripture Challenge card (page 93) and choice and consequence cards (pages 4-6) on colored cardstock paper for each child, scissors, and crayons or markers.

ACTIVITY: Play the Choice and Consequences match game to show what can happen when we make good and bad choices. Notice the pointed cards are the choices and the indented cards are the consequences (making it easier to match). (1) Color and cut out Choice and Consequence cards, mix them up and lay face down. (2) Divide children into two teams. Take turns turning cards over to make a match. The team with the most matches wins.

SCRIPTURE CHALLENGE: Do activity in class or at home.

THOUGHT TREAT: Choose the Right Crackers. Give each child four soda crackers. Ask each child to make up three good choices and one bad choice. As children share the three good choices have them eat their crackers. When tell the one bad choice have them crush one cracker into a bowl symbolizing they do not want that choice.

**Primary 6* manual is published by The Church of Jesus Christ of Latter-day Saints, Salt Lake City, Utah.

Live with Heavenly Father and Jesus

Have a physical body

Be with our family

Learn about Heavenly Father's plan

Have the scriptures to guide us

Experience hard work, sorrow and death

Have only a spirit body

Be able to have children

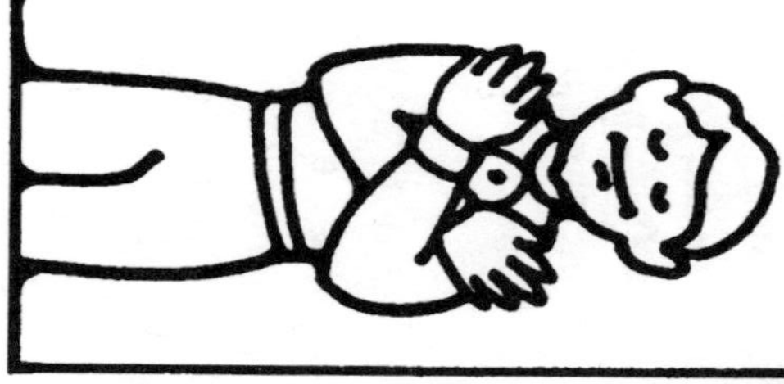

Death

Birth

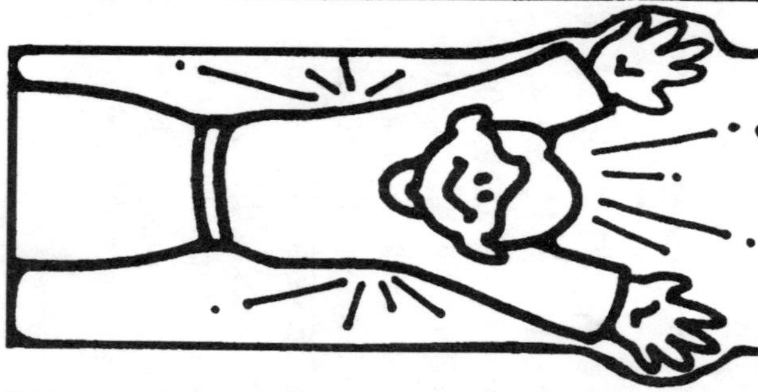

Resurrection

The Plan of Salvation

Final Judgment

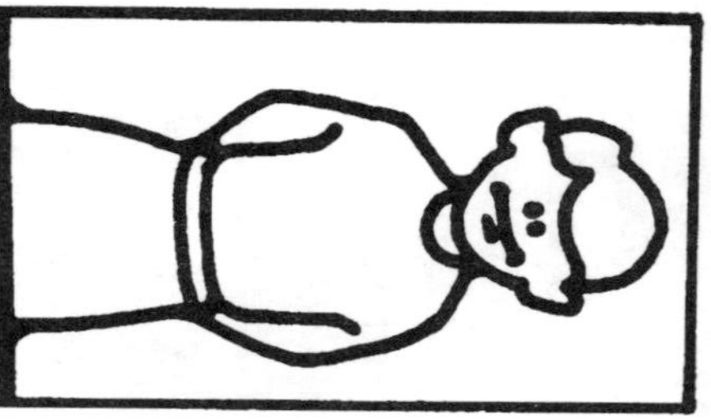

Terrestrial Kingdom

Telestial Kingdom

Celestial Kingdom

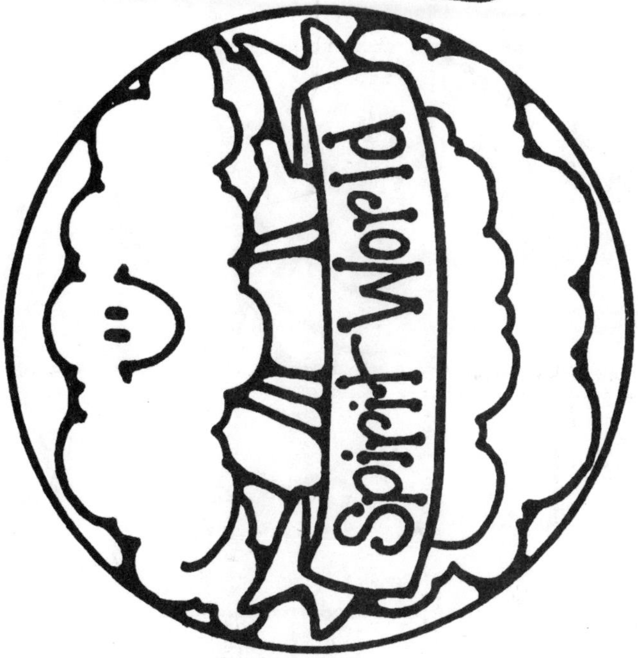
Spirit World

Premortal Life

Earth

Obey the Word of Wisdom

Enjoy good health

Love others

Others will love you

Be reverent in church

Feel Heavenly Father's spirit

Pray

Receive Heavenly Father's help

Attend church

Learn the gospel

Tell a lie

Others will not trust you

Be happy at home

Home is a better place to be

Steal or cheat

Lose the help of the Holy Ghost

Be kind to a new neighbor

Make a new friend

*Lesson #3** CREATION: Heavenly Father and Jesus Created the Earth for Me

(Days 1-7 Creation scripture puzzle)

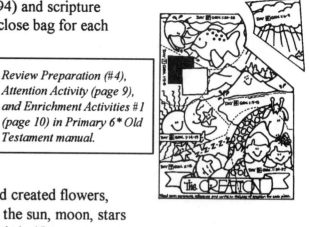

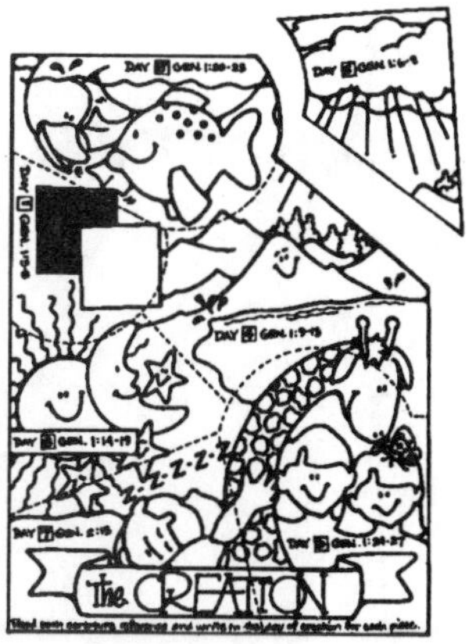

YOU'LL NEED: Copy of Scripture Challenge card (page 94) and scripture puzzle (page 8) on cardstock paper, and an envelope or zip-close bag for each child, scissors, and crayons or markers.

Review Preparation (#4), Attention Activity (page 9), and Enrichment Activities #1 (page 10) in Primary 6 Old Testament manual.*

ACTIVITY: Help children learn the order of the creation. (1) Color and cut out creation puzzle. (2) Read each scripture reference and write in the day it was created. (3) Place puzzle pieces in a bag to store. Children can use this as a teaching tool.

DAYS 1-7 CREATION: On **<u>Day #1</u>**, God divided light and darkness (Gen. 1:3-5); **<u>Day #2</u>,** he created the heavens (Gen. 1:6-8); **<u>Day #3</u>**, he divided land and water, and created flowers, trees, fruit and vegetables (Gen. 1:9-13); **<u>Day #4</u>**, he created the sun, moon, stars (Gen. 1:14-19); **<u>Day #5</u>**, he created fish, water animals, and birds (Gen. 1:20-23); **<u>Day #6</u>**, he created animals and man (Gen. 1:24-27); and **<u>Day #7</u>**, he rested (Gen. 2:1-3).

SCRIPTURE CHALLENGE: Do activity in class or at home.

THOUGHT TREAT: <u>Land and Sea Bread Balls</u>. Roll raised bread dough into 2-3" balls. Roll part of dough ball in cinnamon and sugar mixture (1/3 cinnamon, 2/3 sugar). Roll the other part of the dough ball in blue sugar (mix 2-3 drops food coloring in 1 cup sugar). Bake bread balls 20 minutes at 350° oven. Remind children that the land and water were created on Day #3. Quiz children on what was created on the other five days (detailed above).

*Lesson #4** ETERNAL LIFE: I Will Return to My Heavenly Home

(I Can Return maze)

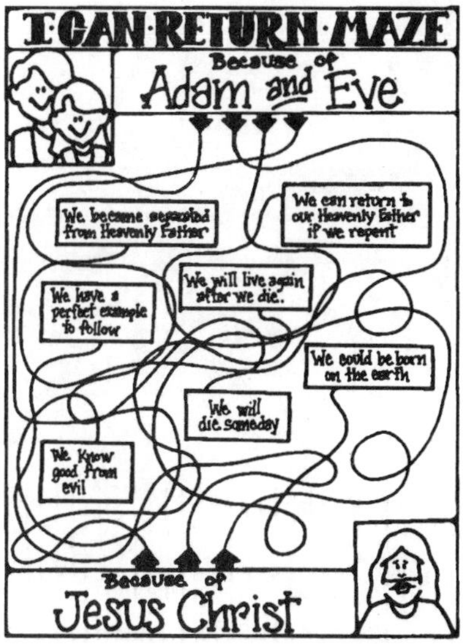

YOU'LL NEED: Copy of Scripture Challenge card (page 94) and maze (page 9) for each child and crayons or markers.

Review Enrichment Activity #3 (page 16) in Primary 6 Old Testament manual.*

ACTIVITY: (1) Help children learn the second article of faith: "We believe that men will be punished for their own sins, and not for Adam's transgression." (2) Using two different colored markers, follow each arrow to find what Adam and Eve and Jesus Christ did to help us gain immortality and eternal life.

<u>Because of Adam and Eve</u>: "We could be born on the earth, we know good from evil, we become separated from Heavenly Father, and we will die someday." **<u>Because of Jesus Christ</u>:** "We will live again after we die, we can return to Heavenly Father if we repent, and we have a perfect example to follow."

SCRIPTURE CHALLENGE: Do activity in class or at home.

THOUGHT TREAT: <u>Eternal Life Licorice Rope</u>. Give each child a two-foot string of licorice to eat as you talk about the straight and narrow path that leads to eternal life. Read 2 Nephi 31:18. Straighten out the licorice piece. Talk about the many temptations that come as we journey back to the presence of our Heavenly Father, how you can stay on the straight path, and how to say "no" to temptation.

**Primary 6* manual is published by The Church of Jesus Christ of Latter-day Saints, Salt Lake City, Utah.

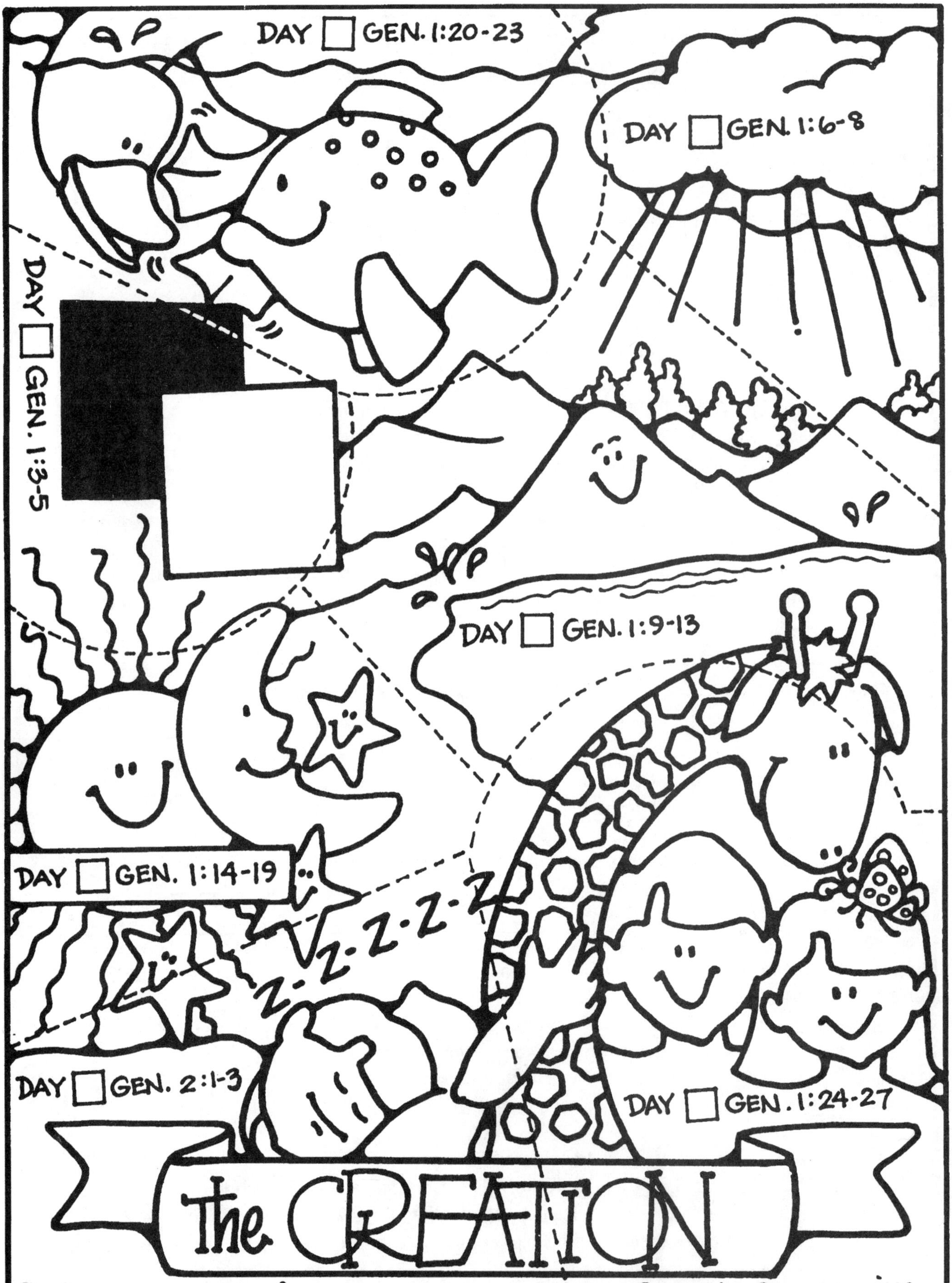

Read each scripture reference and write in the day of creation for each piece.

I CAN RETURN MAZE

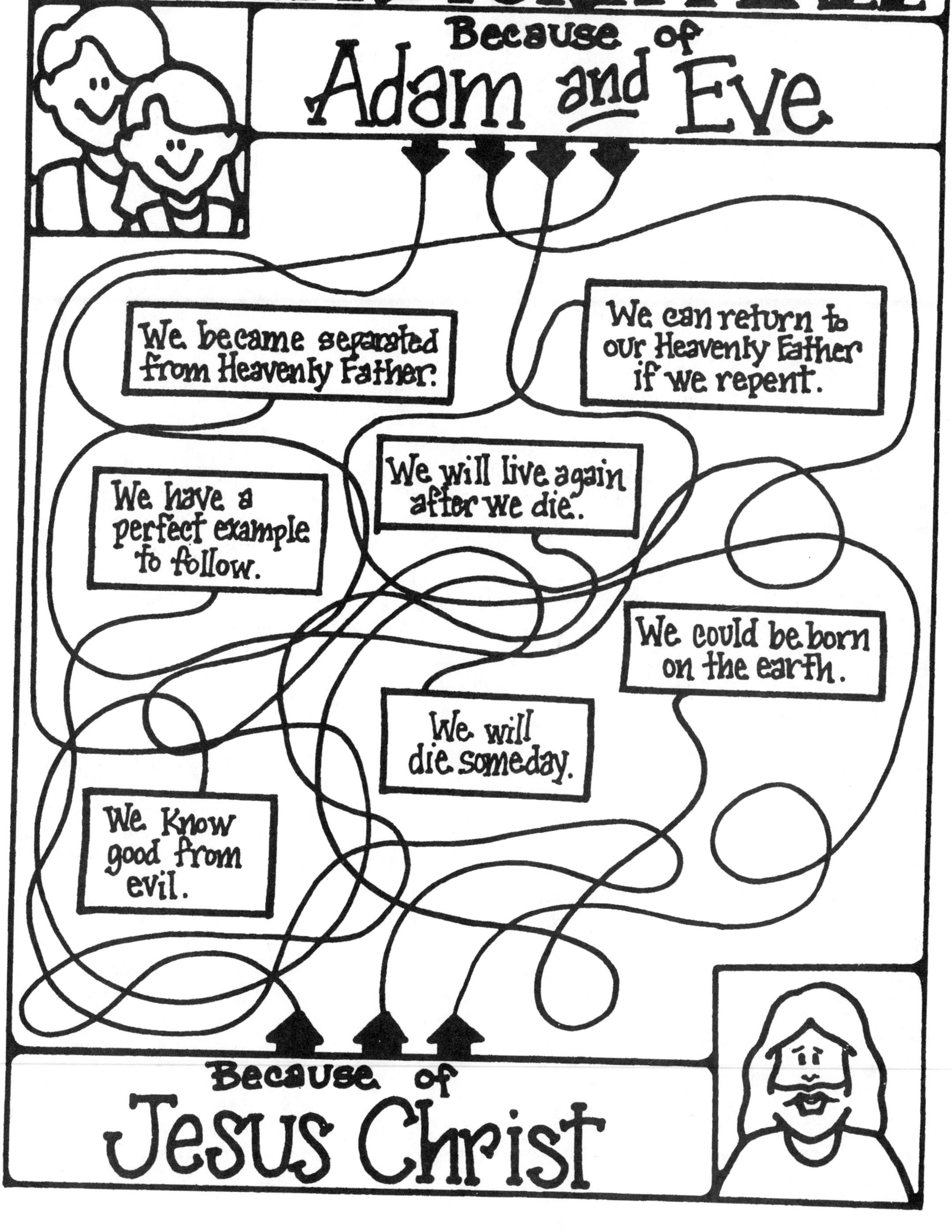

Lesson #5* **SACRIFICE: I Will Always Remember Jesus**

(Tic-Tac-Toe Do You Know?)

YOU'LL NEED: Copy of Scripture Challenge card (page 95), Tic-Tac-Toe game board, Adam and Eve markers, and question wordstrips (pages 11-12), and Tic-Tac-Toe Do You Know rules below for each child, scissors, and crayons or markers.

ACTIVITY: Help children find the missing words in the 15 question wordstrips (also found in the manual* on page 21). **TO MAKE GAME:** (1) Color and cut out a set of 12 Adam and Eve markers and game board. (2) Cut up questions wordstrips.

Review Enrichment Activity #1 (page 20) in Primary 6 Old Testament manual.*

TO PLAY TIC-TAC-TOE DO YOU KNOW?: (1) Divide children into two teams. Give one team Adam markers and the other team Eve markers. (2) Take turns reading a question wordstrip and guessing the missing word. If the guess is right, the player places an Adam or Eve marker on the board. (3) If the guess is wrong, look up scripture and read it aloud to learn the missing word. (4) The first team to place three Adam or Eve squares in a row (either horizontally, diagonally, or vertically) wins the game. (5) When a team wins, remove the markers and start again until questions/scriptures #1-15 are read.

SCRIPTURE CHALLENGE: Do activity in class or at home.

THOUGHT TREAT: Tic-Tac-Toe Waffles. A waffle looks much like a tic-tac-toe game board. Give each child a waffle to place M&M candies inside each square to play Tic-Tac-Toe. Divide into two teams and take turns playing the game. Play with two different colors of candies (one for each team). As you place a marker in the waffle square, name a way you can remember Jesus. IDEAS: See the Enrichment Activity #3 in the *Primary 6** Old Testament manual, page 22. Examples: Put a picture of Jesus in their room, keep scriptures close to bed, bring scriptures to church, say personal prayers, say family prayers, have family home evening, listen to sacrament prayers, pay tithing, serve others, be a missionary, and keep the commandments.

Lesson #6* **ETERNAL LIFE: I Will Live the Gospel of Jesus Christ**

(Faithful Footsteps goal flip chart)

YOU'LL NEED: Copy of Scripture Challenge card (page 95) and flip charts (pages 13-15) for each child, scissors, glue, and crayons.

ACTIVITY: Help children follow in the footsteps of Jesus as they endure to the end.

Review Enrichment Activity #7 (page 26) in Primary 6 Old Testament manual.*

(1) Color and cut out goal flip cards. (2) Glue cards together placing the first, second, third, fourth, and fifth chart behind the first so that footsteps show below each chart (with Faithful Footstep Flip Chart at the top. (3) Write things you can do on each chart to keep that commandment. Remember that each step brings you closer to eternal life, life with Heavenly Father and Jesus. (4) Read 2 Nephi 31:20. *"Press forward"* means to walk in the steps of Jesus, to do as He would do. As we *"press forward,"* enduring to the end, we shall have the greatest of all gifts, eternal life (to live with Heavenly Father and Jesus).

SCRIPTURE CHALLENGE: Do activity in class or at home.

THOUGHT TREAT: Footstep Cookies. Create a frosting footprint in the center of a sugar cookie.

**Primary 6* manual is published by The Church of Jesus Christ of Latter-day Saints, Salt Lake City, Utah.

Tic-Tac-Toe

Do You Know?

1. Adam's sacrifices were a _ _ _ _ _ _ _ _ _ _ _ of the sacrifice of the Only Begotten of the Father. (Moses 5:6-7)

2. Adam and Eve's son _ _ _ _ was a tiller of the ground. (Moses 5:17)

3. Abel was a keeper of _ _ _ _ _. (Moses 5:17)

4. Cain loved _ _ _ _ _ more than God. (Moses 5:18)

5. Abel offered as a sacrifice the _ _ _ _ _ _ _ _ _ _ _ of his flock. (Moses 5:20)

6. Cain's offering was the _ _ _ _ _ of the ground. (Moses 5:19)

7. The Lord did not accept Cain's _ _ _ _ _ _ _ _ (Moses 5:21)

8. Satan promised to deliver Abel into Cain's hands if he would swear to keep a _ _ _ _ _ _ (Moses 5:29-30)

9. When the Lord asked Cain where Abel was, Cain said: "I know not. Am I my brother's _ _ _ _ _ _?" (Moses 5:34)

10. FREE POINT

11. FREE POINT

12. The Lord set a _ _ _ _ on Cain so that people who saw him would know that they must not harm him. (Moses 5:40)

13. The sacrament took the place of _ _ _ _ _ _ sacrifice after the death of Jesus Christ. (Alma 34:13)

14. The gospel was taught from the beginning by angels, God's own voice, and by the gift of the _ _ _ _ _ _ _ _ _ _. (Moses 5:58)

15. "As many as believed in the Son, and _ _ _ _ _ _ _ _ _ of their sins, should be saved." (Moses 5:15)

Faithful Footsteps Flip Chart

I will follow in the footsteps of Jesus Christ

I will endure to the end as I....

My tithing goals are:

____

____

____

____

____

Pay my tithing

My prayer goals are:

____

____

____

Pray to Heavenly Father

My church attendance goals are: ______________

____

____

____

____

____

____

Attend church

My scripture reading goals are: ______________

____

____

____

____

____

____

____

Read the scriptures

PATTERN: *ETERNAL LIFE (Faithful Footsteps goal flip chart)*

*Lesson #7**

ZION: I Will Be Pure in Heart to Help Build Zion

(Pure in Heart Game)

YOU'LL NEED: Copy of Scripture Challenge card (page 96), I Love Zion label and heart wordstrips (page 17) on cardstock, and a zip-close plastic bag for each child, scissors, and crayons.

Review Enrichment Activity #5 (page 30) in Primary 6 Old Testament manual.*

ACTIVITY: Help children decide which actions bring them closer to Zion and those that keep them from Zion. Zion will be a place of safety where Jesus will come and live. Evil people cannot live there. The city will be beautiful. Everyone there will love Heavenly Father. Everyone will love each other. Zion will be a happy place where peace comes to all who are pure in heart (D&C 45:64-71). **TO MAKE GAME:** Color and cut out label and wordstrips and place them in a zip-close plastic bag. See game rules on label. Encourage children to take this activity home to share with their family.

SCRIPTURE CHALLENGE: Do activity in class or at home.

THOUGHT TREAT: Heart-Shaped Cookies. Tell children if their hearts are in the right place, loving the things of the Lord, they will be able to practice living a Zion type of life in their own homes.

*Lesson #8**

PROPHET:

I Will Listen to and Follow the Prophet

(Noah and the Ark word search)

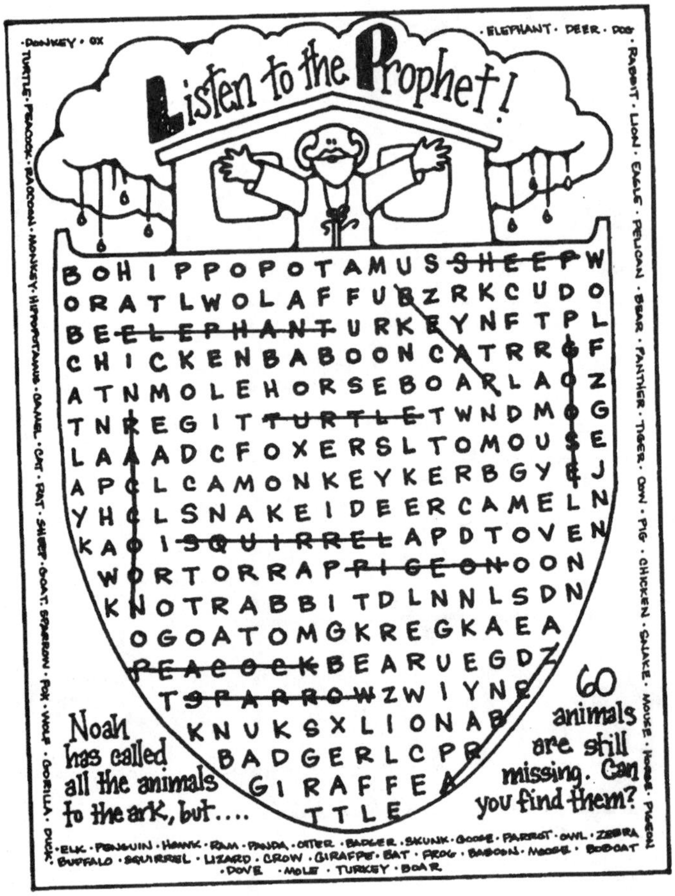

Review Lesson (pages 31-32) in Primary 6 Old Testament manual.*

YOU'LL NEED: Copy of Scripture Challenge card (page 96) on colored cardstock paper, and Noah word search (page 18) for each child, pencils, and crayons or markers.

ACTIVITY: Color word search and help Noah find the 60 missing animals.

SCRIPTURE CHALLENGE:
Do activity in class or at home.

THOUGHT TREAT:
Animal Cookies. Ask children to name their favorite animals and tell why they like them.

*Primary 6 manual is published by The Church of Jesus Christ of Latter-day Saints, Salt Lake City, Utah.

I LOVE

TO PLAY: (1) Divide class into two teams. (2) Take turns reading a heart message aloud to your team. (3) Team says, "Pure in heart" if the action is positive, helping you to build up Zion. (4) Team says, "Takes away purity" if the action is negative, one that does not build Zion. I love Zion!

PURE IN HEART GAME

I spent my afternoon talking with a lonely neighbor.	I stepped on a worm on purpose.
I told my mother "thank you" for a wonderful dinner.	I spent my tithing on toys and candy.
I didn't yell at the dog even though he chewed up my shoe.	I yelled at my parents and slammed the door.
I forgave my friend for calling me a name.	I fed my sister's cat.
I worked hard on my homework so I would know the answers.	I borrowed my friend's nail polish and didn't return it.
I read a story to my sister.	I didn't pay my mother back the money I borrowed.
I mowed my neighbor's lawn.	I took some candy without asking.
I did the dishes without being asked.	I told my friend I would call him when I knew I wouldn't call.
I taught my younger sister to tie her shoes.	I shoved my brother.
I read my scriptures daily.	I left garbage in my yard.
I make sincere prayer a daily habit.	I told my brother he was stupid.
I thought bad thoughts about my brother.	I wouldn't let my sister wear my sweater because it is mine!

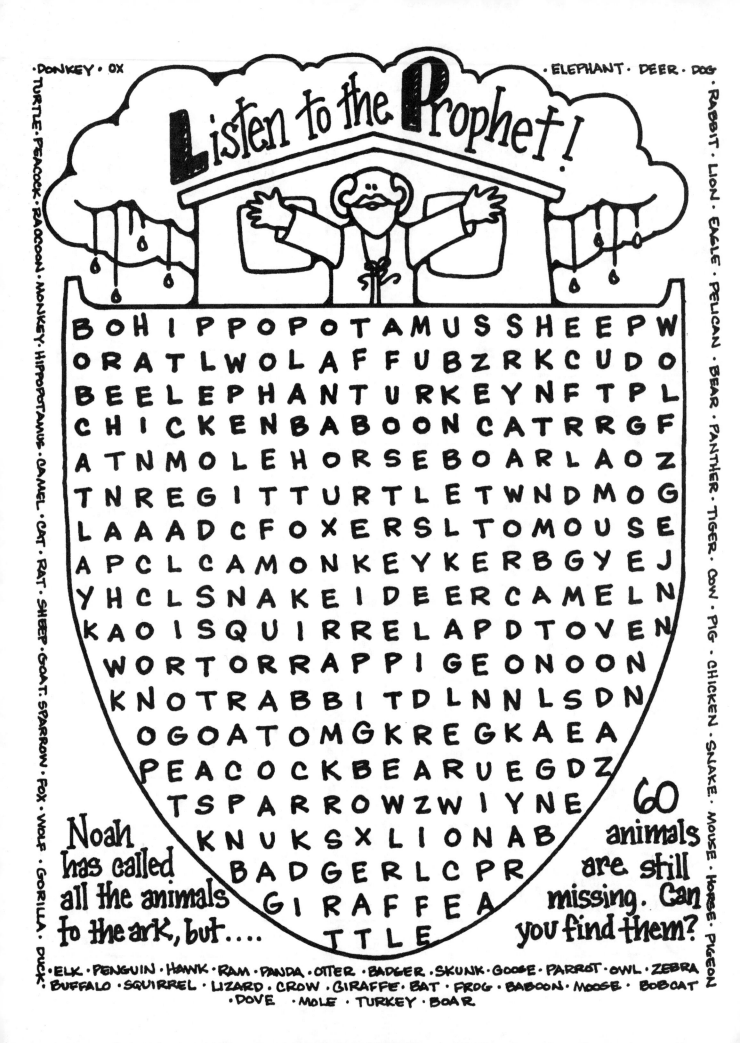

Listen to the Prophet!

DONKEY · OX · ELEPHANT · DEER · DOG · RABBIT · LION · EAGLE · PELICAN · BEAR · PANTHER · TIGER · COW · PIG · CHICKEN · SNAKE · MOUSE · HORSE · PIGEON

TURTLE · PEACOCK · RACCOON · MONKEY · HIPPOPOTAMUS · CAMEL · CAT · RAT · SHEEP · GOAT · SPARROW · FOX · WOLF · GORILLA · DUCK

B O H I P P O P O T A M U S S H E E P W
O R A T L W O L A F F U B Z R K C U D O
B E E L E P H A N T U R K E Y N F T P L
C H I C K E N B A B O O N C A T R R G F
A T N M O L E H O R S E B O A R L A O Z
T N R E G I T T U R T L E T W N D M O G
L A A A D C F O X E R S L T O M O U S E
A P C L C A M O N K E Y K E R B G Y E J
Y H C L S N A K E I D E E R C A M E L N
K A O I S Q U I R R E L A P D T O V E N
W O R T O R R A P P I G E O N O O N
K N O T R A B B I T D L N N L S D N
O G O A T O M G K R E G K A E A
P E A C O C K B E A R U E G D Z
T S P A R R O W Z W I Y N E
K N U K S X L I O N A B
B A D G E R L C P R
G I R A F F E A
T T L E

Noah has called all the animals to the ark, but….

60 animals are still missing. Can you find them?

ELK · PENGUIN · HAWK · RAM · PANDA · OTTER · BADGER · SKUNK · GOOSE · PARROT · OWL · ZEBRA · BUFFALO · SQUIRREL · LIZARD · CROW · GIRAFFE · BAT · FROG · BABOON · MOOSE · BOBCAT · DOVE · MOLE · TURKEY · BOAR

*Lesson #9**

MISSION: I Will Prepare for My Mission

(Missionary Doors scripture search)

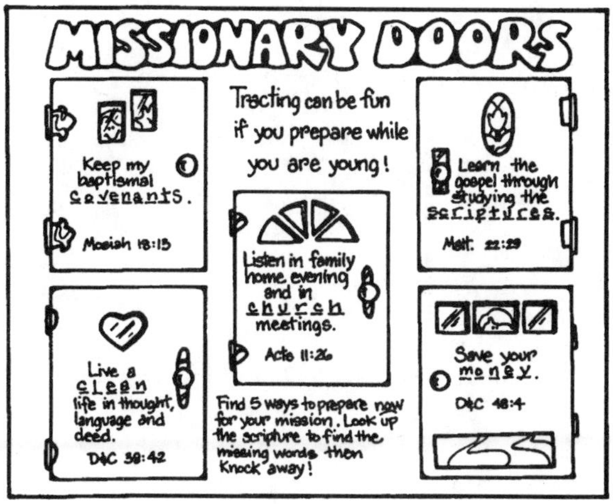

YOU'LL NEED: Copy of Scripture Challenge card (page 97) on colored cardstock paper, and Missionary Doors scripture search (page 20) for each child, pencils, scriptures, and crayons or markers.

Review Enrichment Activity #4 (page 37) in Primary 6 Old Testament manual.*

ACTIVITY: Help children learn five ways they can prepare now to share the gospel on a full-time mission when they are older. Read the scriptures to fill in the missing words.

ANSWERS: Mosiah 18:13 (keep covenants), D&C 38:42 (be clean), Acts 11:26 (go to church), Matthew 22:29 (study scriptures), and D&C 48:4 (save money). Abraham 2:10 explains that those who become members of The Church of Jesus Christ of Latter-day Saints will be a part of Abraham's seed (children). They shall be blessed.

SCRIPTURE CHALLENGE: Do activity in class or at home.

THOUGHT TREAT: Door to Door Sandwich. Make a cream cheese sandwich (mix room temperature cream cheese with jam or jelly). Spread on bread and cut off crust. Cut sandwich in half. Stick a round piece of candy on left side for doorknob. Have children practice asking the golden questions: "What do you know about The Church of Jesus Christ of Latter-day Saints? Would you like to know more?"

*Lesson #10**

LOVE: I Will Show Love to Others as I Serve

(My Circle of Love Spin-and-Serve game)

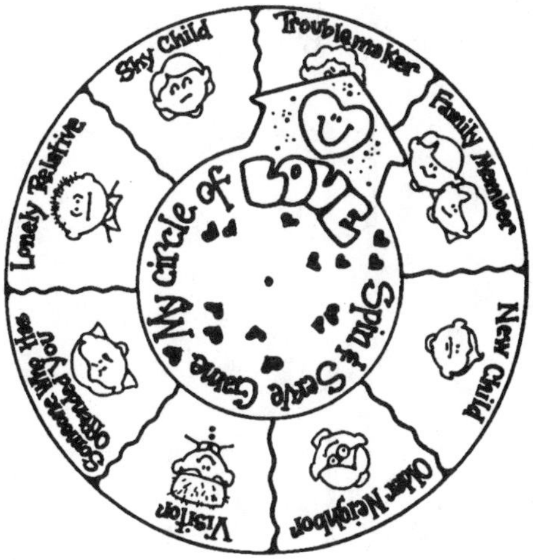

YOU'LL NEED: Copy of Scripture Challenge card (page 97), game parts A and B (page 21) on colored cardstock paper, and a metal or button brad for each child, and crayons or markers.

ACTIVITY: Create a Circle of Love Spin-and-Serve Game to talk about ways children can include others in their circle of love. (1) Color and cut out circle parts A and B. (2) Attach part A to part B (larger circle) with a metal or button brad. To make a button brad, sew two buttons together on opposite sides (threading thread through the same hole) to attach wheel parts A and B. (3) Child spins the center circle, then tells about the person the arrow is pointing to on the board. Children tell others how they will love and serve that person to include them in their circle of love.

Review Enrichment Activities #3 and #4 (pages 41-42) in Primary 6 Old Testament manual.*

SCRIPTURE CHALLENGE: Do activity in class or at home.

THOUGHT TREAT: Circle of Love Cookies. Decorate round cookies with a frosted heart. As children eat, ask them to think of someone they will include in their circle of love.

Primary 6 manual is published by The Church of Jesus Christ of Latter-day Saints, Salt Lake City, Utah.

MISSIONARY DOORS

Tracting can be fun if you prepare while you are young!

Keep my baptismal __________S.

Mosiah 18:13

Learn the gospel through studying the ___________.

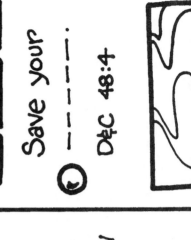

Matt. 22:29

Listen in family home evening and in ________ meetings.

Acts 11:26

Live a _____ life in thought, language and deed.

D&C 38:42

Save your ______.

D&C 48:4

Find 5 ways to prepare now for your mission. Look up the scripture to find the missing words then Knock away!

PART A

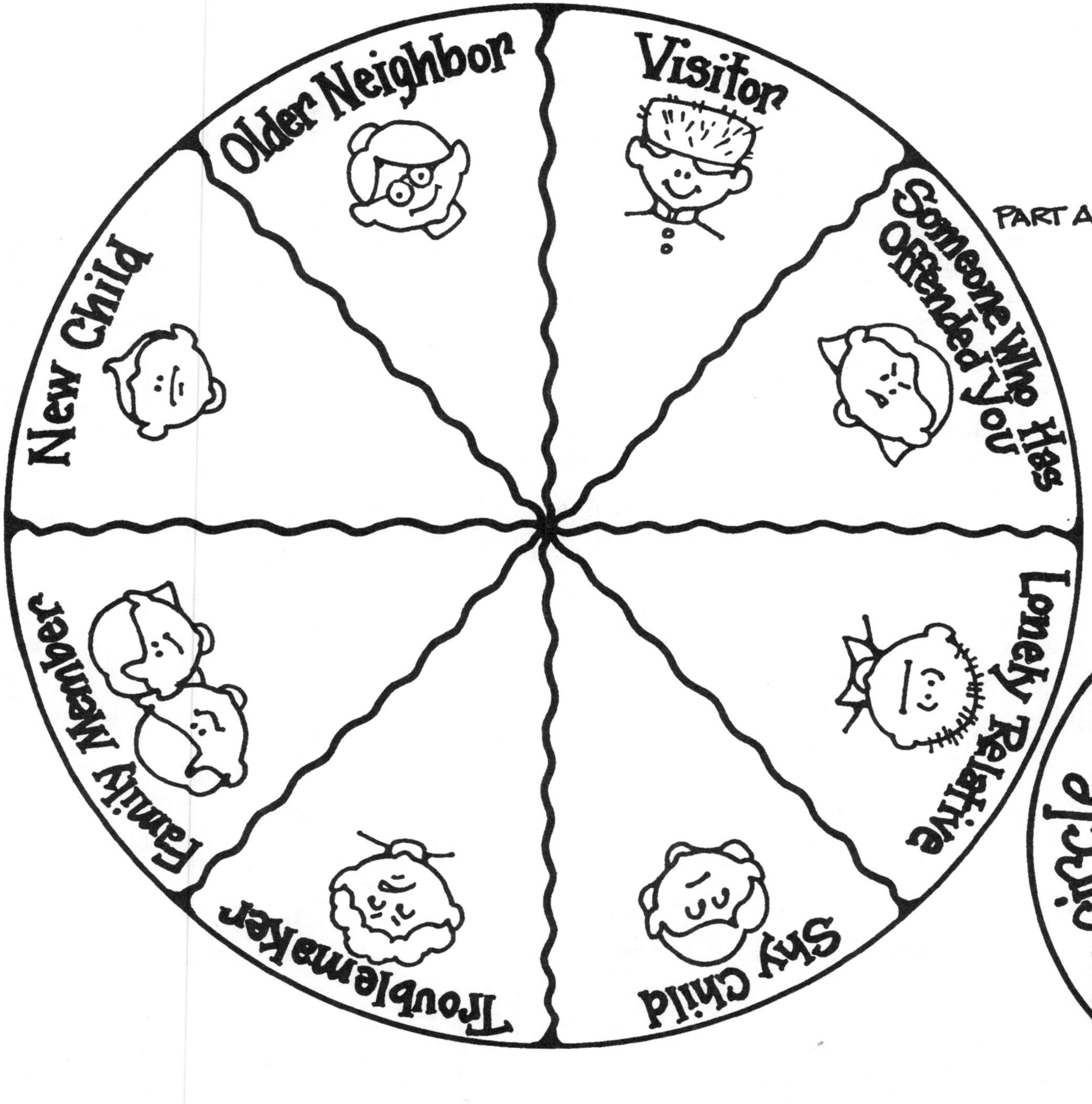
Older Neighbor
Visitor
Someone Who Has Offended You
Lonely Relative
Shy Child
Troublemaker
Family Member
New Child

PART B

My circle of LOVE
Spin & Serve Game

*Lesson #11**	**TRUST: I Believe in Heavenly Father and Jesus Christ** *(Trust in the Lord bite-size memorize)*

YOU'LL NEED: Copy of Scripture Challenge card (page 98) on colored cardstock paper, and bite-size memorize poster (page 23) for each child, scriptures, and crayons or markers.

Review Enrichment Activity #2 and #3 (page 45) in Primary 6 Old Testament manual.*

ACTIVITY: Help children learn to trust in Heavenly Father and Jesus and do the following to show their trust (see border of poster).
(1) Color and read poster using the scriptures.
(2) Encourage children to memorize Proverbs 3:5-6.

SCRIPTURE CHALLENGE: Do activity in class or at home.

THOUGHT TREAT: Confidence Cookies. Share a cookie with children and ask them, "Do you have confidence or trust that what I am telling you is true? The best way to know the truth is to read the scriptures and pray, asking Heavenly Father to give you a feeling of peace and joy if these things are true. The spirit of the Holy Ghost will give you a sweet, peaceful feeling. There is a certain sweetness that comes from having your own testimony, just like these sweet Confidence Cookies. Another way to gain confidence is to live the commandments to be worthy of truth and God's blessings."

*Lesson #12**	**TEMPLE MARRIAGE Brings Eternal Blessings** *(Together Forever righteous ring)*

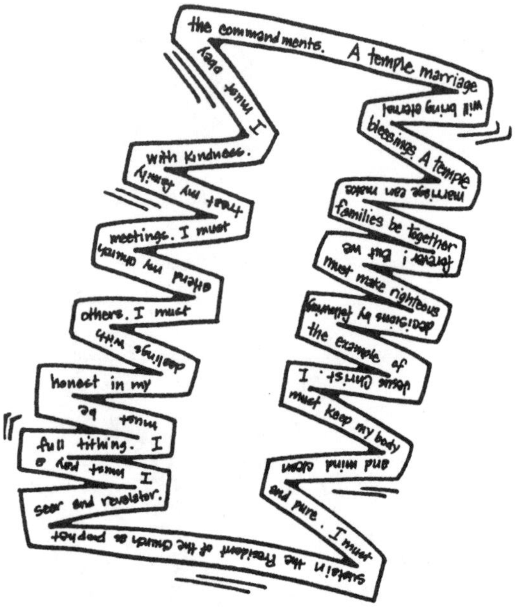

YOU'LL NEED: Copy of Scripture Challenge card (page 98), righteous ring (page 24) on colored cardstock paper for each child, scissors, and a stapler or tape.

Review Preparation #3 and Attention Activity (page 47) and Enrichment Activity #5 (page 51) in Primary 6 Old Testament manual.*

ACTIVITY: Create a Together Forever righteous ring. (1) Cut out outside edge. (2) Fold in half lengthwise. (3) Cut center fold line 1/8 inch where indicated (leaving fold tab uncut). (4) Cut into lines left and right, being careful not to cut through to the other side. (5) Pull into circle shape. Have children place the ring over their heads as you read the message starting with "A temple marriage will bring eternal blessings," and the ending reads, "I must obey the commandments." The circle or ring represents eternal blessings that can be found if we follow the righteous actions on ring.

SCRIPTURE CHALLENGE: Do activity in class or at home.

THOUGHT TREAT: Eternity Ring Doughnuts. Serve cake doughnuts (without frosting) that represent eternal marriage, having no end, lasting forever and ever if both husband and wife obey Heavenly Father's commandments and keep their covenants.

**Primary 6* manual is published by The Church of Jesus Christ of Latter-day Saints, Salt Lake City, Utah.

BITE SIZE MEMORIZE

Trust in the Lord with all thine heart; and lean not unto thine own understanding. In all ways acknowledge him, and he shall direct thy paths.

Proverbs 3:5-6

fold

commandments.
I must obey the
family with kindness.
must treat my
meetings. I
attend my church
others. I must
dealings with
honest in my
I must be
a full tithing.
I must pay
and revelator.
prophet, seer
the church as
President of
sustain the
pure. I must

A temple
marriage will
bring eternal
blessings.
A temple
marriage can
make families
be together
forever!
But we must
make righteous
decisions by
following the
example of
Jesus Christ.
I must keep
my body and
mind clean and

fold

*Lesson #13** CHOOSE THE RIGHT To Keep Heaven in Sight
(thumb puppets)

YOU'LL NEED: Copy of Scripture Challenge card (page 99) and thumb puppets on colored cardstock paper (page 26) for each child, scissors, tape, and crayons or markers.

> *Review Enrichment Activity #3 (pages 54-55) in Primary 6* Old Testament manual.*

ACTIVITY: Talk about Jacob, who obeyed the commandments, making thumbs-up choices, and Esau, who sold his birthright for a mess of pottage, making thumbs-down choices (Genesis 25:30-32).

TO PLAY: Jacob chose the right, so place a Jacob (thumbs-up) puppet on the right hand and an Esau (thumbs-down) puppet on the left hand of each child. Read the following actions as children vote thumbs-up for right actions, and thumbs-down for wrong choices.

CHOICES: Going to a movie on the Sabbath ↘ Saying a prayer at mealtime ↗ Cheating on a test ↘ Reading the scriptures each day ↗ Being a friend to someone who doesn't have friends ↗ Complaining when it's time for family home evening ↘ Cleaning up after yourself ↗ Doing your chores cheerfully ↗ Smoking ↘ Listening reverently in Primary ↗ Listening to your little brother or sister ↗ Working hard to get your homework done each day ↗ Going to a friend's house after school without permission ↘ Forgetting to call your parents when you get to your friend's house ↘ Making a get-well card for a sick neighbor ↗ Smiling ↗ Sweeping the garage without being asked ↗ Spending tithing money ↘ Watching a bad movie ↘ Listening to uplifting music ↗ Saying please and thank you ↗ Staying up too late ↘ Eating junk food often ↘ Repenting ↗

SCRIPTURE CHALLENGE: Do activity in class or at home.

THOUGHT TREAT: Thumb Print Cookies. Tell children that thumbs-up means "good going." Let's try each day to make thumbs-up choices.

*Lesson #14** HONESTY: I Will Make and Keep Good Promises
(Honesty Pays Blessing Bucks board game)

YOU'LL NEED: Copy of Scripture Challenge card (page 99) and Honesty Pays game board (page 27-28), on colored cardstock paper, 4 copies each of Blessing Bucks, team #1 and #2 markers, move #1-4 wordstrip (page 28) on green lightweight paper, and a small envelope or plastic bag for each child, scissors, and crayons or markers.

> *Review Enrichment Activity #2 (page 58) in Primary 6* Old Testament manual.*

ACTIVITY: Help children learn the difference between good promises and bad promises. Even though children may be honest about keeping their promises, some promises are good and some are bad. Blessings come from keeping good promises. Color and cut out game pieces and play by the rules (page 28). Tell children that the word "bucks" means money (in paper bills), which is a temporal reward, but Blessing Bucks are spiritual rewards that come from making and keeping good promises. Honesty pays because you feel good about the promises you make and others trust you.

SCRIPTURE CHALLENGE: Do activity in class or at home.

THOUGHT TREAT: Honest Heart Candies. Tell children that honesty comes from the heart.

**Primary 6* manual is published by The Church of Jesus Christ of Latter-day Saints, Salt Lake City, Utah.

Jacob

Esau

Jacob

Esau

Jacob

Esau

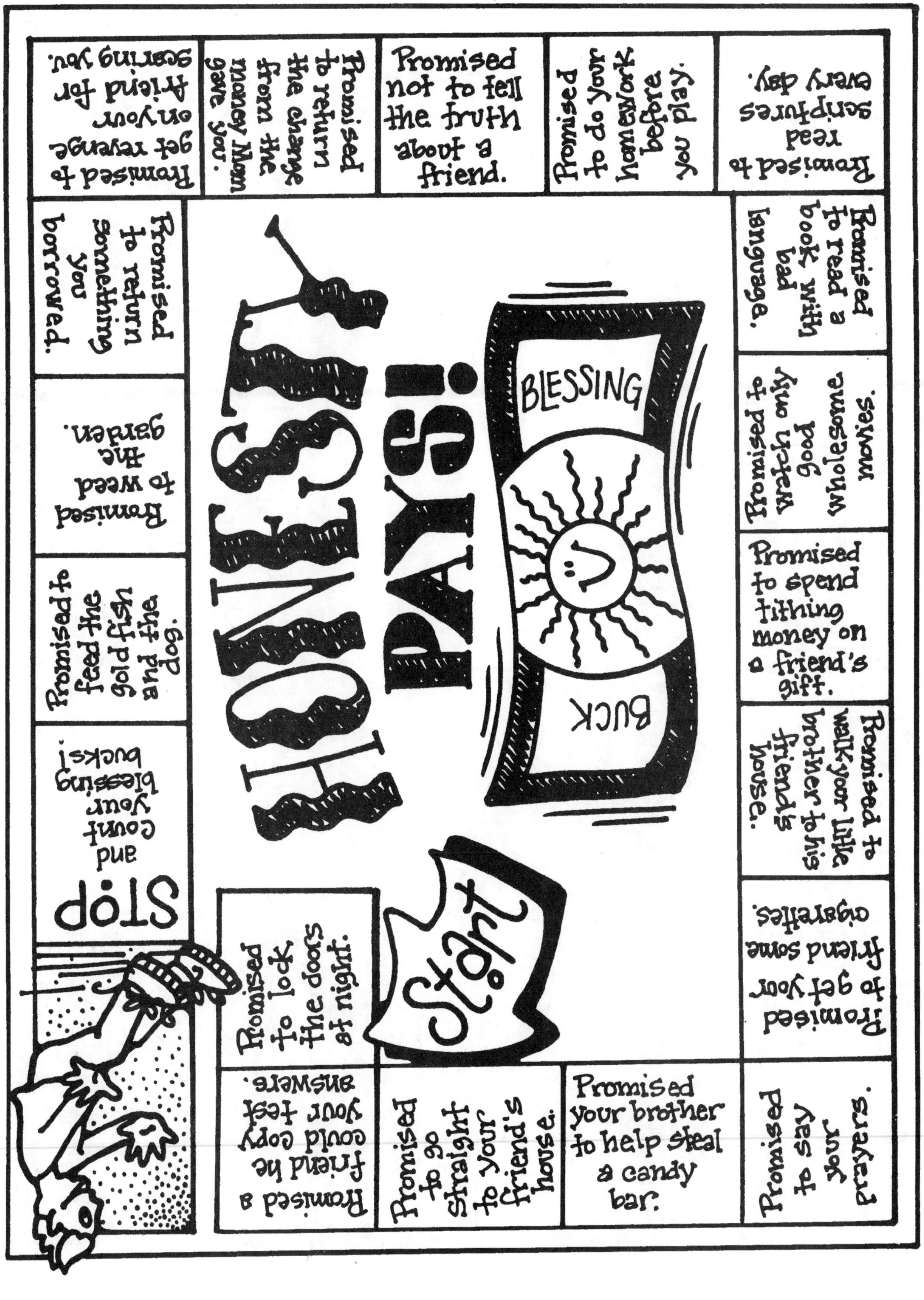
HONESTY PAYS!
BLESSING
BUCK
Start
Promised to lock the doors at night.
Promised a friend he could copy your test answers.
Promised to go straight to your friend's house.
Promised your brother to help steal a candy bar.
Promised to say your prayers.
Promised to get your friend some cigarettes.
Promised to walk your little brother to his friend's house.
Promised to spend tithing money on a friend's gift.
Promised to watch only good wholesome movies.
Promised to read a book with bad language.
Promised to read scriptures every day.
Promised to do your homework before you play.
Promised not to tell the truth about a friend.
Promised to return the change from the money Mom gave you.
Promised to get revenge on your friend for scaring you.
Promised to return something you borrowed.
Promised to weed the garden.
Promised to feed the gold fish and the dog.
STOP and count your blessing bucks!

GAME RULES:

1. Divide class into two teams, using buttons or coins for markers at the START position.
2. Take turns drawing a move marker and moving to that position on the board.
3. Read the promise and decide if the promise is a good promise or a bad promise.

☹ If it is a <u>bad promise</u>, tell what the consequence is for making that bad promise.

☺ If it is a <u>good promise</u>, tell what the consequence is for following through on a good promise, and collect a Blessing Buck.

4. TO WIN! Count up the score after someone reaches "STOP and Count Blessing Bucks." The team with the most Blessing Bucks wins!

Back 2	Move 3	Move 2	Move 1
Back 1	Move 3	Move 2	Move 1
Back 2	Move 3	Move 2	Move 1
Back 1	Move 3	Move 2	Move 1
Back 2	Move 3	Move 2	Move 1
Back 2	Move 3	Move 2	Move 1
Back 1	Move 3	Move 2	Move 1

*Lesson #15** ATTITUDE: My Faith in Jesus Christ Gives Me Courage

(mirror motivators)

YOU'LL NEED: Copy of Scripture Challenge card (page 100) and mirror motivators (page 30) on colored cardstock paper for each child, and crayons or markers.

Review Enrichment Activity #3 (page 65) in Primary 6 Old Testament manual.*

ACTIVITY: Encourage children to color and post these four motivators on their mirror at home to remind them to be happy, to have faith in God, and to make the best of every situation.

SCRIPTURE CHALLENGE: Do activity in class or at home.

THOUGHT TREAT: Sour Lemons to Lemonade. Make a batch of lemonade to share. First slice and let children taste a lemon. Then place sugar on their slice of lemon. Tell them that as they add sugar to lemonade it makes it sweet, just as our faith in Jesus Christ sweetens our testimony. *Review Enrichment Activity #2 (page 64) in Primary 6* Old Testament manual.* Tell children that by having faith in Jesus Christ they can have courage to make life sweet.

*Lesson #16** CHOOSE THE RIGHT: I Will Stay Away from Evil

(Decision Drama)

YOU'LL NEED: Copy of Scripture Challenge card (page 100) on colored cardstock paper, Look Ahead Decision Drama bag label and wordstrips (page 31), an envelope or plastic bag for each child, scissors, and crayons or markers. Make up one set using a jar and lid (shown right).

Review Enrichment Activities: #1, #2, and #4 (pages 69-70) in Primary 6 Old Testament manual.*

ACTIVITY: Tell children that if they think ahead before a temptation comes, they will know what to do. They will know how to stop and say "no" to temptation. Example: Joseph ran from Potipher's wife (Genesis 39:8-10, 12).

TO MAKE: Color and cut out labels and wordstrips. Glue one label on a jar and place wordstrips inside to play. If you make one for each child, choose from the following options. #1: Place label and wordstrips in a plastic bag. #2: Place wordstrips in an envelope and glue label to the outside of envelope.

TO PLAY: Divide class into two teams. Teams take turns drawing a wordstrip. Player follows the instructions on the label. If the wordstrip reads "GO," pantomime the action (without words). Team tries to guess action. If they guess, award 10 points. If the wordstrip reads "STOP," act out what you would do or say to run away from that temptation, but don't use key words on the wordstrip, i.e. if you say "smoking," you don't receive points. If the wordstrip reads "GO," pantomime the action that keeps your mind and heart pure and see if others can guess the action. The team with the most points wins.

SCRIPTURE CHALLENGE: Do activity in class or at home.

THOUGHT TREAT: STOP and GO Cookies. Frost cookies red and green, and write "STOP" on red cookies and "GO" on green cookies with white frosting in a tube. Tell children that when we say "No" to temptation and say "Yes" to clean and pure actions, we can stay on the heaven-bound road.

**Primary 6* manual is published by The Church of Jesus Christ of Latter-day Saints, Salt Lake City, Utah.

If life gives
me lemons...
I'll make
lemonade!

"A merry heart doeth good
like a medicine: but a broken
spirit drieth the bones."
Proverbs 17:22

"And we know
that all things
work together for
good to them that
love God."
Romans
8:28

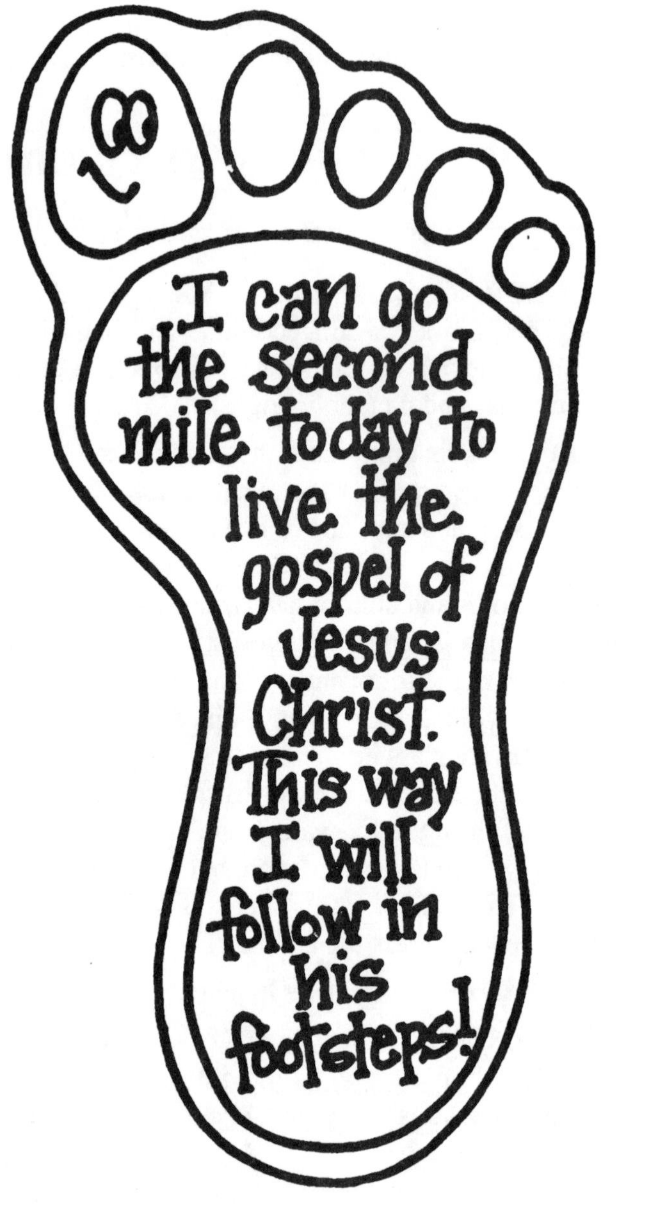
I can go
the second
mile today to
live the
gospel of
Jesus
Christ.
This way
I will
follow in
his
footsteps!

LOOK AHEAD!

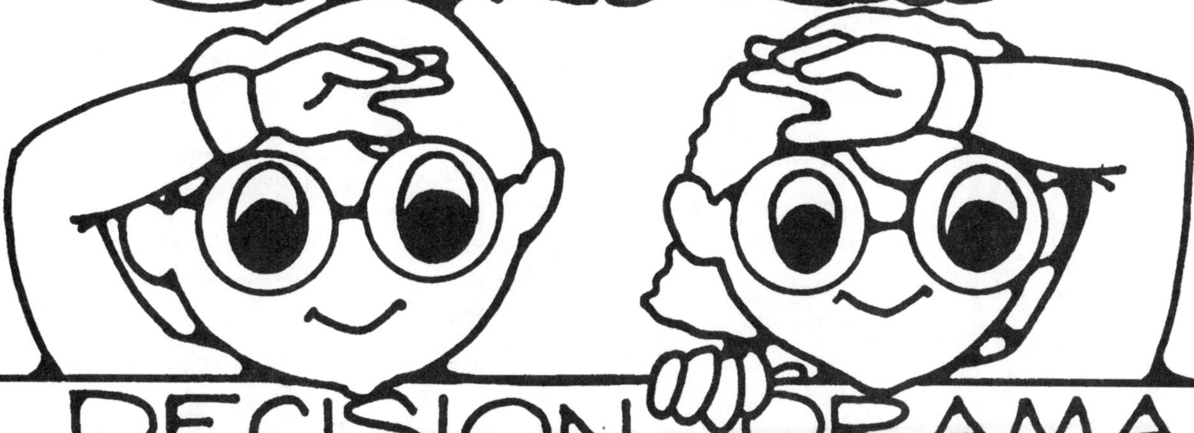

DECISION DRAMA

Take turns drawing a wordstrip.

STOP: Act out what you would do or say to run away from that temptation.

GO: Pantomime the action that keeps your mind and heart pure and see if others can guess the action!

STOP: Reading bad books	STOP: Skipping church	GO: Read a good book
STOP: Gossipping	STOP: Avoiding family home evening	GO: Pay tithing
STOP: Swearing	STOP: Stealing	GO: Sit reverently
STOP: Dressing immodestly	STOP: Spending tithing	GO: Listen to others
STOP: Watching bad shows	STOP: Disobeying parents	GO: Be Kind
STOP: Telling unclean jokes	GO: Attend church	GO: Feed the cat
STOP: Listening to improper songs	GO: Have family home evening	GO: Walk the dog
STOP: Using drugs	GO: Pray	GO: Empty garbage.
STOP: Smoking	GO: Read scriptures	GO: Shine mirrors
STOP: Skipping school	GO: Be honest	GO: Help neighbor mow their lawn
STOP: Sassing parents	GO: Watch uplifting movies	GO: Obey parents

*Lesson #17**	**FORGIVENESS: I Will Forgive Others** *(forgiveness doorknob hanger)*

YOU'LL NEED: Copy of Scripture Challenge card (page 101), forgiveness doorknob hanger (page 33) on colored cardstock paper for each child, scissors, and crayons or markers.

Review Enrichment Activity #1 (page 73) in Primary 6 Old Testament manual.*

ACTIVITY: Help children think about forgiving and unforgiving feelings and how those feelings appear in our faces with this doorknob sign. (1) Color and cut out doorknob sign. (2) Fold sign in half and glue back to back. (3) Draw in forgiving and unforgiving faces.
SCRIPTURE CHALLENGE: Do activity in class or at home.
THOUGHT TREAT: Forgiving Fudge and Popcorn. Create four smiling faces out of fudge (recipe below). Fill a plastic bag with popcorn and four pieces of smile fudge in each bag to represent the four forgiving feelings: peaceful, happy, loving, and friendly. Ask children to search through the popcorn to find the four forgiving faces. As they eat the Forgiving Fudge, name the four forgiving feelings. TO MAKE FUDGE SMILES: Melt an 11-ounce package of milk chocolate chips, 7-ounces sweetened condensed milk, and 1 tsp. vanilla in the microwave (about 2-6 minutes). While hot, drop by teaspoons full onto waxed paper. Mold into balls, then press balls to 1/4". Carve a smile with the edge of a spoon. Place round candy pieces for the eyes.

*Lesson #18**	**PREPARING for My Life's Mission** *(Mission Statements match game)*

YOU'LL NEED: Copy of Scripture Challenge card (page 101) and two sets each of now and future match cards (pages 34-35) on colored cardstock paper for each child, scissors, and crayons.

Review Enrichment Activity #5, (page 78) in Primary 6 Old Testament manual.*

ACTIVITY: Say to children, "Should you choose to accept your mission in life to prepare for the celestial kingdom, you will need to do the following." (Read from cards or mission statement below.)
MISSION STATEMENT: Things I Am Doing Now: Receiving baptism, attending church, serving others, working hard, praying with purpose. Things I Will Do in the Future: Serve a mission, marry in the temple, teach children the gospel, learn another language, receive my patriarchal blessing, build the kingdom of God on the earth.
TO PLAY THE MATCH GAME: Lay two sets of cards face down, with class sitting in a circle. Take turns turning two cards over to make a match. The one with the most matches wins. Talk about each action and how it helps us fulfill our mission here on earth. This way we can be ready to live in the celestial kingdom with Heavenly Father and Jesus when that time comes.
SCRIPTURE CHALLENGE: Do activity in class or at home.
THOUGHT TREAT: M&M Mission Statements. Offer 12 M&M candies as children each name one action to prepare for our mission in life—what they can do now and in the future (as described on the mission statement cards).

**Primary 6* manual is published by The Church of Jesus Christ of Latter-day Saints, Salt Lake City, Utah.

When I do
FORGIVE
I feel.....
peaceful
happy
loving
friendly
When I do not
FORGIVE
I feel.....
angry
jealous
unhappy
critical

DO IN THE FUTURE
Serve a mission

DO IN THE FUTURE
Marry in the temple

DO IN THE FUTURE
Teach my children the gospel

DO IN THE FUTURE
Learn another language

DO IN THE FUTURE
Receive my patriarchal blessing

DO IN THE FUTURE
Build the Kingdom of God on earth

DOING NOW
Receiving Baptism

DOING NOW
Attending church

DOING NOW
Reading scriptures

DOING NOW
Serving others

DOING NOW
Working hard

DOING NOW
Praying with purpose.

*Lesson #19**

PRIESTHOOD Is the Power of God

(Egyptian Plagues crossword puzzle)

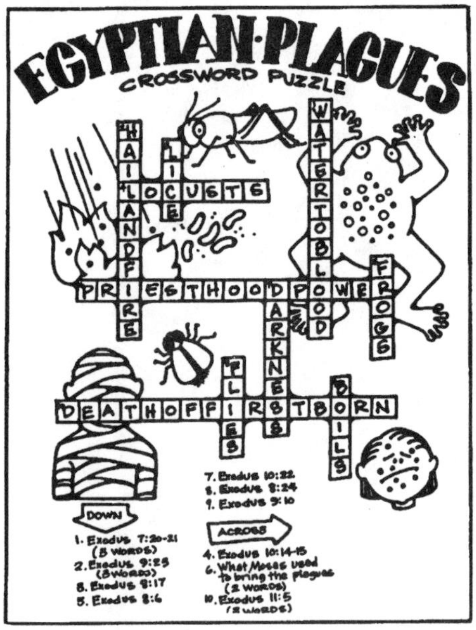

YOU'LL NEED: Copy of Scripture Challenge card (page 102) on colored cardstock paper, and Egyptian Plagues puzzle (page 37) for each child, pencils, and crayons or markers.

ACTIVITY: Help children learn the ten plagues the Lord told Moses to inflict upon the Egyptians (using his priesthood power). Remind children that the plagues were sent to tell the Egyptians to free the Israelites from slavery.

Review Enrichment Activity #1 (page 83) in Primary 6 Old Testament manual.*

1. Color the puzzle.
2. Find the down and across words by reading the scriptures.

ANSWERS: Down: (1) water to blood (2) hail and fire (3) lice (5) frogs (7) darkness (8) flies (9) boils Across: (4) locusts (6) priesthood power (10) death of firstborn

SCRIPTURE CHALLENGE: Do in class or at home.

THOUGHT TREAT: Egyptian Mummy Marshmallows. Push toothpicks into five large marshmallows to make a mummy-like image. Tell children that the Egyptians wrapped their dead in white linen and placed them in the large tombs. These large tombs were built by the Israelite slaves while they were in slavery.

*Lesson #20**

SABBATH DAY Is a Day of Worship and Joy

(Sabbath Day Activity advent calendar)

YOU'LL NEED: Copy of Scripture Challenge card (page 102) and advent calendar with wordstrips (page 38) on colored cardstock paper for each child, scissors, glue, yarn, paper punch, zip-close sandwich bags, and crayons or markers.

ACTIVITY: Challenge children to try these 14 activities on the Sabbath Day to keep it holy. Each Sunday you might ask children to share their experiences with the activities.

Review Enrichment Activity #3 (page 87) in Primary 6 Old Testament manual.*

1. Color and cut out advent calendar (cutting wordstrips at the bottom on the dotted line).
2. Punch holes at the top of calendar and tie a 20" piece of yarn to hang it on the wall.
3. Fill a zip-close plastic sandwich bag with 14 small pieces of candy children can enjoy after trying each Sabbath Day activity. Read instructions on the calendar.

SCRIPTURE CHALLENGE: Do activity in class or at home.

THOUGHT TREAT: Welcomed Wilderness Manna. Serve some bread in the shape of rolls to look like the manna provided by the Lord to the Israelites (Exodus 16:11-15, 19-20).

**Primary 6* manual is published by The Church of Jesus Christ of Latter-day Saints, Salt Lake City, Utah.

EGYPTIAN·PLAGUES
CROSSWORD PUZZLE

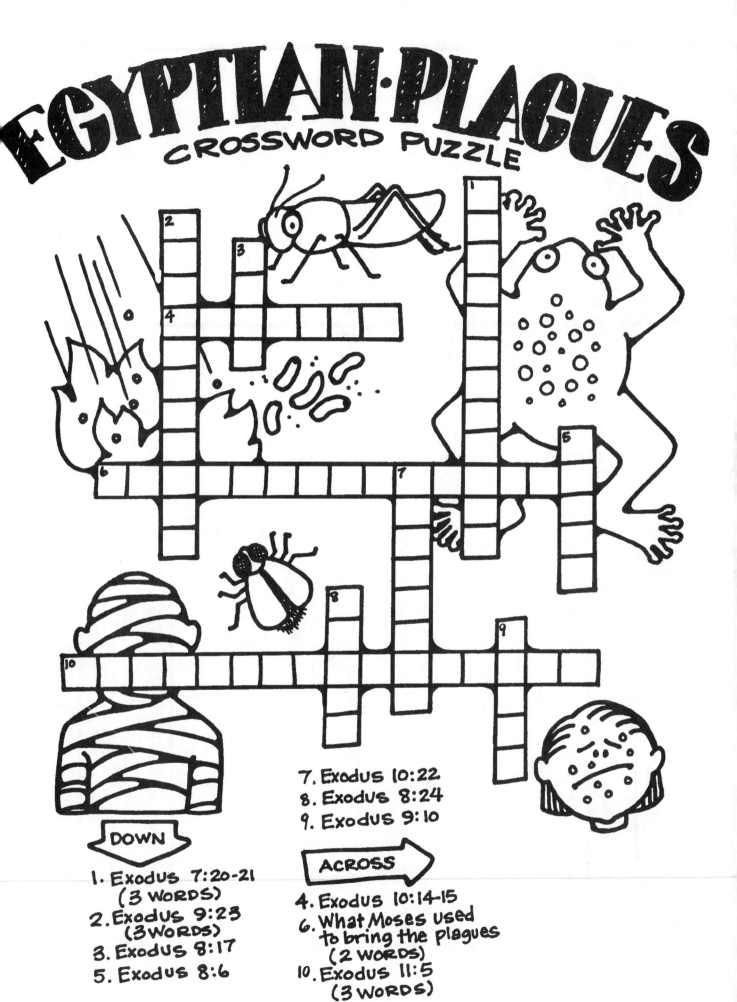

7. Exodus 10:22
8. Exodus 8:24
9. Exodus 9:10

DOWN

1. Exodus 7:20-21 (3 WORDS)
2. Exodus 9:23 (3 WORDS)
3. Exodus 8:17
5. Exodus 8:6

ACROSS

4. Exodus 10:14-15
6. What Moses used to bring the plagues (2 WORDS)
10. Exodus 11:5 (3 WORDS)

SABBATH DAY

ACTIVITY · ADVENT · CALENDAR

14 days 14 ways

to Keep the Sabbath Day holy!

Try an activity and tear off the wordstrip below. Then enjoy a treat in the bag and say, "It's sweet to honor the Sabbath Day!"

1. Write a letter to a missionary.
2. Visit an older member in the ward.
3. Read a scripture story to brother or sister.
4. Write in your journal.
5. Listen to sacred music.
6. Study the scriptures.
7. Visit relatives.
8. Give a family home evening lesson.
9. Play quiet games with your brother or sister.
10. Read your baby journal or family history.
11. Look at family photographs.
12. Visit someone who is ill or lonely.
13. Take turns acting out and guessing scripture stories.
14. Make cards of appreciation for family members.

*Lesson #21** **COMMANDMENTS Bring Light to My Life**
(10 Commandments key word cake)

Review Attention Activity (page 90) and Discussion of Commandments #1-10 (page 91) in Primary 6 Old Testament manual.*

YOU'LL NEED: Copy of Scripture Challenge card (page 103) on colored cardstock paper, and key word cake (page 40) for each child, pencils, and crayons or markers.

ACTIVITY: Talk about the ingredients that make a cake and compare it to the 10 Commandments, the "ingredients" God gave to Moses. Living the ten commandments will make your life sweet. It will also bring light to our life, just like the candles that light up a cake. Tell children that obeying the commandments can be a "piece of cake," or as easy as 1, 2, 3. Here's how: (1) Read the scriptures daily to learn about the commandments of God. (2) Pray to know what you should do to keep the commandments. (3) Listen to the Spirit of the Holy Ghost to help you keep the commandments.

TO LEARN COMMANDMENT KEY WORDS: Look up the scripture and write in the key words to the 10 Commandments on the candles. Children can make up their own key words or use these (shown above, reading left to right): Exodus 20:3—Love God, Exodus 20:4—No graven images, Exodus 20:7—No swearing, Exodus 20:8—Keep the Sabbath holy, Exodus 20:12—Obey parents, Exodus 20:13—Do not kill, Exodus 20:14—Be chaste, Exodus 20:15—Do not steal, Exodus 20:16—Do not lie, Exodus 20:17—Do not envy

SCRIPTURE CHALLENGE: Do activity in class or at home.

THOUGHT TREAT: 10 Commandment Cupcakes. Make 10 cupcakes with a candle on each and pretend to light candles. Talk about the Spirit of the Holy Ghost that lights our way when we obey the commandments. The Holy Ghost can also leave (pretend to blow out candles) when we don't obey. As we obey the commandments we build character and become more like Jesus.

*Lesson #22** **HUMILITY: I Am Willing to Be Taught by Others**
(Who is Humble Henry? humility search)

Review Enrichment Activity #1 (page 97) in Primary 6 Old Testament manual.*

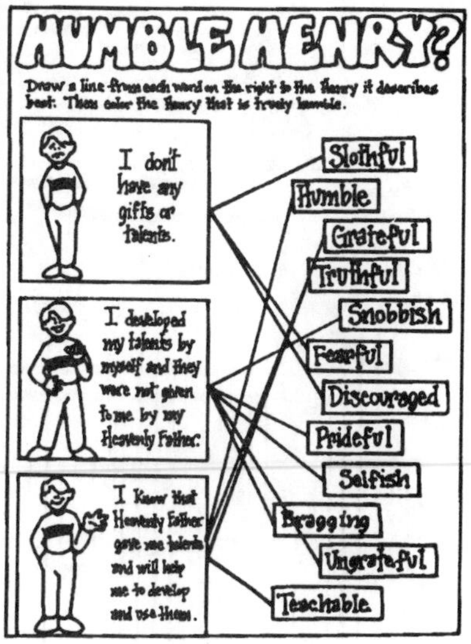

YOU'LL NEED: Copy of Scripture Challenge card (page 103) on colored cardstock paper and Humble Harry? search (page 41) for each child, pencils, and crayons or markers.

ACTIVITY: Help children learn the type of person who is humble and those who are not humble. FIND HUMBLE HENRY: (1) Draw a line from the words on the right to the Henry it describes best. (2) Color the Henry who is truly humble.

SCRIPTURE CHALLENGE: Do activity in class or at home.

THOUGHT TREAT: "Be Humble" Pie. Stick two gumdrop ears into a piece of pie. Tell children that if we listen to others and allow them to teach us, then we are being humble and we can learn God's ways. If we are not humble or teachable, we may end up eating "humble pie." This means that we are forced to admit that we are wrong, which will make us humble the painful way.

**Primary 6* manual is published by The Church of Jesus Christ of Latter-day Saints, Salt Lake City, Utah.

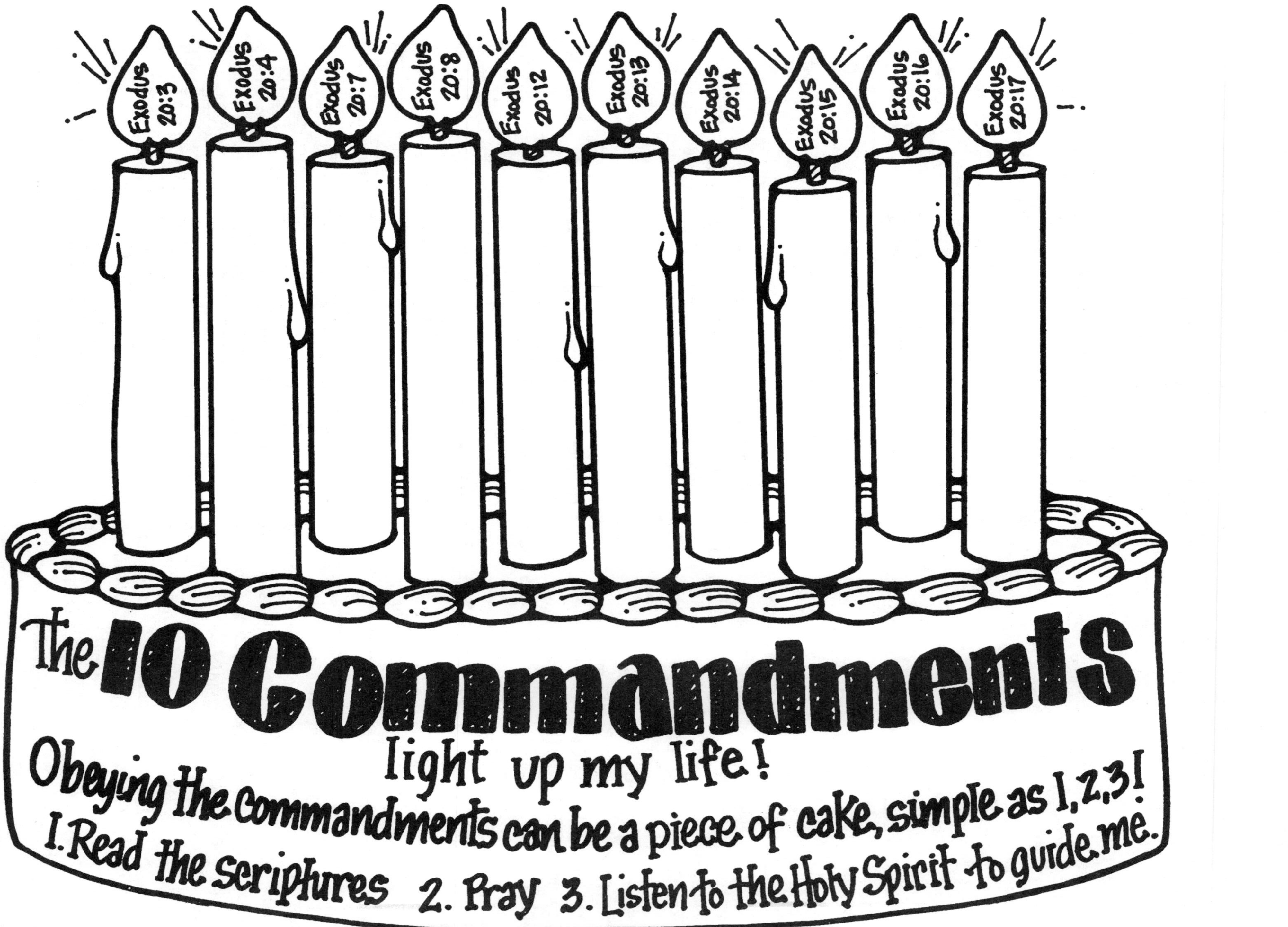
Exodus 20:3
Exodus 20:4
Exodus 20:7
Exodus 20:8
Exodus 20:12
Exodus 20:13
Exodus 20:14
Exodus 20:15
Exodus 20:16
Exodus 20:17
The 10 Commandments
light up my life!
Obeying the commandments can be a piece of cake, simple as 1,2,3!
1. Read the scriptures 2. Pray 3. Listen to the Holy Spirit to guide me.

HUMBLE HENRY?

Draw a line from each word on the right to the Henry it describes best. Then color the Henry that is truely humble.

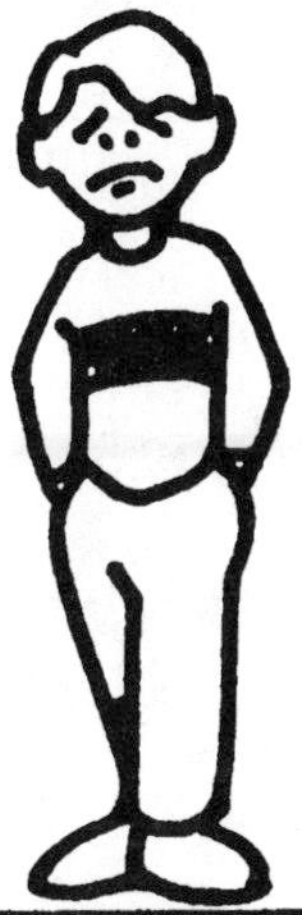

I don't have any gifts or talents.

I developed my talents by myself and they were not given to me by my Heavenly Father.

I Know that Heavenly Father gave me talents and will help me to develop and use them.

Slothful

Humble

Grateful

Truthful

Snobbish

Fearful

Discouraged

Prideful

Selfish

Bragging

Ungrateful

Teachable

*Lesson #23**

HAPPINESS: I Will Find Happiness as I Follow Jesus

(Decision to Follow Jesus Reward list)

YOU'LL NEED: Copy of Scripture Challenge card (page 104) on colored cardstock paper and (follow Jesus) reward list (page 43) for each child, pencils, and crayons or markers.

Review Enrichment Activity #4 (page 104) in Primary 6 Old Testament manual.*

ACTIVITY: Help child make a decision now to serve the Lord by placing a smile (☺) symbol next to the rewards for following Jesus. Then place a frown (☹) symbol next to the consequences for not following Jesus. Color and post this reward list.

SCRIPTURE CHALLENGE: Do activity in class or at home.

THOUGHT TREAT: Happy Heart Cakes. Make cupcakes or muffins. With a tube of red or pink frosting, frost a heart on top with a smile face inside the heart. Tell children that happiness is a feeling that you have in your heart that comes from serving others as Jesus did.

*Lesson #24**

COMMANDMENTS: I Will Trust in the Lord and Obey

(Follow Righteous Leaders Trust-and-Tell game)

YOU'LL NEED: Copy of Scripture Challenge card (page 104), Follow the Leader bean bag label and CTR Challenges wordstrips (page 44), 2 zip-close plastic sandwich bags and beans to fill bag for each child, scissors, and crayons or markers.

Review Enrichment Activities #1 and #3 (page 108) in Primary 6 Old Testament manual.*

ACTIVITY: Help children learn to trust and follow righteous leaders by playing this Follow the Leader Trust and Tell Game.

TO MAKE GAME: (1) Fill a zip-close sandwich bag with beans. Enclose a second bag over bag (for stability). (2) Color and cut out bag label, fold "**GAME RULES**" flap on fold line and fold back. Then place label inside second zip-close sandwich bag. (3) Cut out the Choose the Right Challenges (wordstrips) and enclose in the back half of the bag (opposite the label). (4) Read the rules on the bag and play the game.

OPTION TO GAME: Have child write answers on the blank "Righteous Leader Says" line.

SCRIPTURE CHALLENGE: Do activity in class or at home.

THOUGHT TREAT: School of Fish Follow-the-Leader Snacks. Serve fish crackers or fish gummy candy and tell children that these fish are following their leader. We too follow our leaders. We can know who we should follow by listening to the still small voice of the Holy Ghost. This special guide will always be there to show us the way, if we continue to keep the commandments.

**Primary 6* manual is published by The Church of Jesus Christ of Latter-day Saints, Salt Lake City, Utah.

I choose to follow Jesus.

My Decision To Follow Jesus Reward List

Place a smile next to the reward for following Jesus. Place a frown next to the consequences for not following him.

- ◯ We are miserable.
- ◯ The Holy Ghost stays around us.
- ◯ We can resist temptation.
- ◯ We lose our faith.
- ◯ We lose our spiritual blessings.
- ◯ Our faith increases.
- ◯ We are blessed spiritually.
- ◯ We are happy.
- ◯ The Holy Ghost will not guide us.
- ◯ It is harder for us to resist temptation.

PATTERN: *COMMANDMENTS (Follow Righteous Leaders Trust and Tell Game)*

GAME RULES

1. Players stand in a circle.
2. Toss the bag to a person standing in the circle.
3. That person draws a CTR Challenge wordstrip out of the bag and reads it aloud. This is a temptation we might face. OPTION: Instead of drawing a wordstrip, name a tempting situation on your own.
4. That person tells others what a trusted righteous leader would ask you to do. Example: CTR Challenge: "Asked to smoke a cigarette." A righteous leader says: "Obey the Word of Wisdom."

CTR CHALLENGE: **ASKED TO SMOKE A CIGARETTE.** RIGHTEOUS LEADER SAYS: ____________	CTR CHALLENGE: **ASKED TO TAKE DRUGS.** RIGHTEOUS LEADER SAYS: ____________
CTR CHALLENGE: **ASKED TO DRINK BEER.** RIGHTEOUS LEADER SAYS: ____________	CTR CHALLENGE: **TEMPTED NOT TO READ SCRIPTURES.** RIGHTEOUS LEADER SAYS: ____________
CTR CHALLENGE: **ASKED TO SHOP ON SUNDAY.** RIGHTEOUS LEADER SAYS: ____________	CTR CHALLENGE: **ASKED TO STEAL SOMETHING.** RIGHTEOUS LEADER SAYS: ____________
CTR CHALLENGE: **TEMPTED TO CHEAT ON A TEST.** RIGHTEOUS LEADER SAYS: ____________	CTR CHALLENGE: **TEMPTED NOT TO PRAY.** RIGHTEOUS LEADER SAYS: ____________
CTR CHALLENGE: **TEMPTED TO SKIP CHURCH.** RIGHTEOUS LEADER SAYS: ____________	CTR CHALLENGE: **TEMPTED TO SPEND TITHING MONEY.** RIGHTEOUS LEADER SAYS: ____________
CTR CHALLENGE: **TEMPTED TO TELL A LIE.** RIGHTEOUS LEADER SAYS: ____________	CTR CHALLENGE: **TEMPTED TO SWEAR.** RIGHTEOUS LEADER SAYS: ____________
CTR CHALLENGE: **TEMPTED TO TALK DURING SACRAMENT MEETING.** RIGHTEOUS LEADER SAYS: ____________	CTR CHALLENGE: **TEMPTED TO NOT HELP AT HOME.** RIGHTEOUS LEADER SAYS: ____________

*Lesson #25** COVENANTS: I Will Develop Spiritual Strength

(Sink or Swim slide-show)

YOU'LL NEED: Copy of Scripture Challenge card (page 105) on colored cardstock paper, and Sink or Swim puppet slide-show and wordstrips (pages 46-47) for each child, pencils, and markers.

Review Enrichment Activity #3 (page 112) in Primary 6 Old Testament manual.*

ACTIVITIES: Tell children when we are baptized into The Church of Jesus Christ of Latter-day Saints, we make promises, or covenants, to keep God's commandments. By keeping the commandments we gain spiritual strength to swim the sea of life. We can either sink or swim. If we make and keep righteous promises, we can swim safely back to our heavenly home. If we don't keep the commandments, we sink into the depths of despair.

SINK OR SWIM SLIDE-SHOW: (1) Color and cut out pull-through puppet. (2) Cut slits in the top and bottom of puppet. (3) Slide puppet through. (4) Cut out the sink or swim wordstrips and place them face down. (5) Divide into two teams and take turns drawing a wordstrip. Read the wordstrip and guess "sink" or "swim," by pulling the puppet up or down.

SINK ANSWERS: #2, 3, 5, 7, 9, 10, 11, 15, 16, 18, 22.
SWIM ANSWERS: #1, 4, 6, 8, 12, 13, 14, 17, 19, 20, 21.

SCRIPTURE CHALLENGE: Do activity in class or at home.

THOUGHT TREAT: Sailor's Sandwich. Create a sandwich or half a sandwich for each child. Create a cheese sail by placing a slice of cheese on top (cut diamond shape) attached with a toothpick. Tell children that they can keep their spirit from drowning in the sea of life if they remember to keep their baptismal covenants. Read Mosiah 18:8-10.

*Lesson #26** EXAMPLE: I Will Choose Good Examples to Follow

(Portrait of My Spiritual Hero)

YOU'LL NEED: Copy of Scripture Challenge card (page 105), and portrait (page 48) on colored cardstock paper for each child, pencils, and crayons or markers.

Review Enrichment Activity #1 (page 116) in Primary 6 Old Testament manual.*

ACTIVITY: Encourage children to draw a portrait of their spiritual hero. Then write the traits that hero has and the actions they wish to follow.

SCRIPTURE CHALLENGE: Do activity in class or at home.

THOUGHT TREAT: Footstep Fudge. Microwave melt 1 (11.5 oz.) package milk chocolate chips or butterscotch chips with 4 ounces sweetened condensed milk, and 1/2 teaspoon vanilla. Melt 2-3 minutes and stir. Roll into fudge balls (1 tablespoon each). Shape into feet and add 5 miniature chocolate chips for toes. Tell children that as they follow in the footsteps of their spiritual heroes, they too become spiritual hereos for others to follow.

**Primary 6* manual is published by The Church of Jesus Christ of Latter-day Saints, Salt Lake City, Utah.

PATTERN: *COVENANTS (Sink or Swim puppet show puppet)*

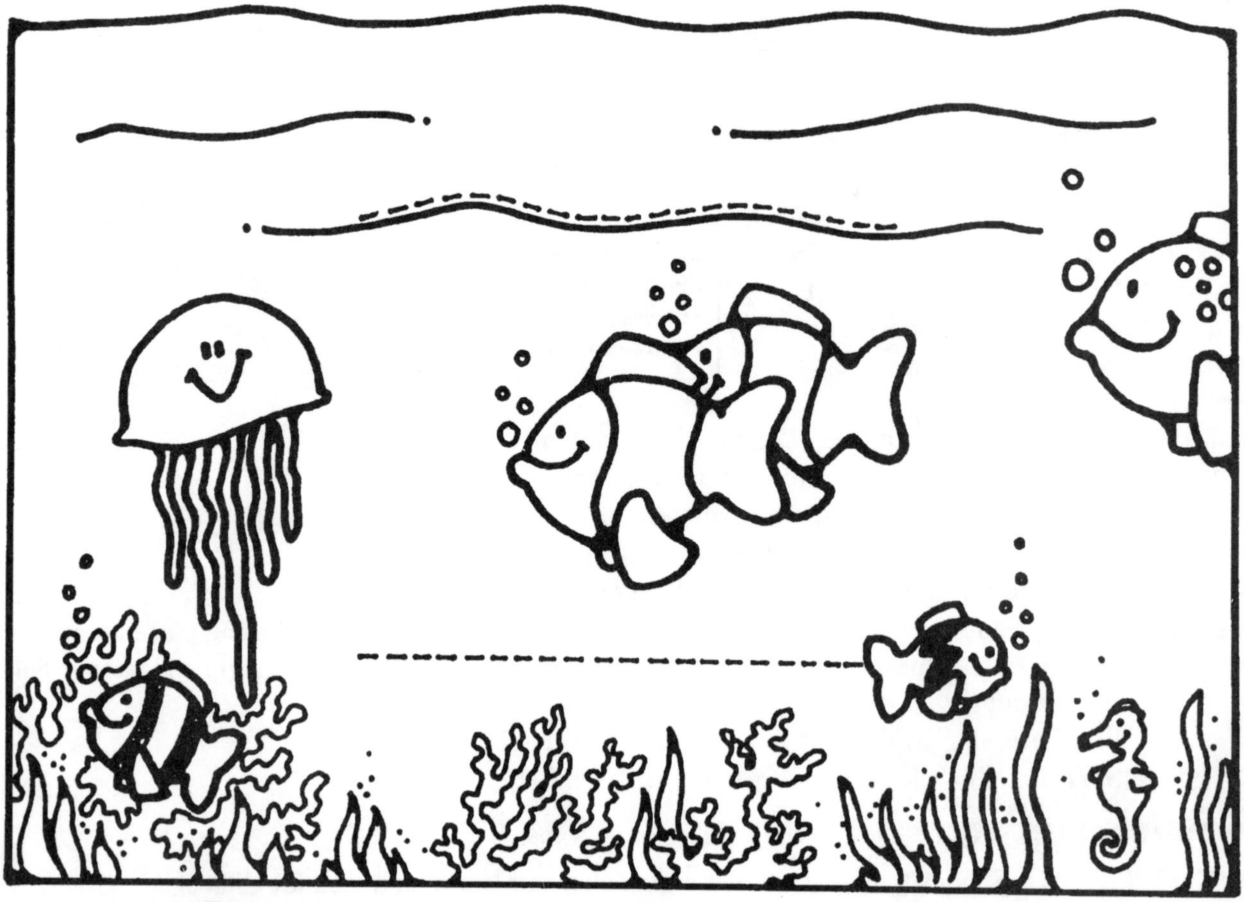

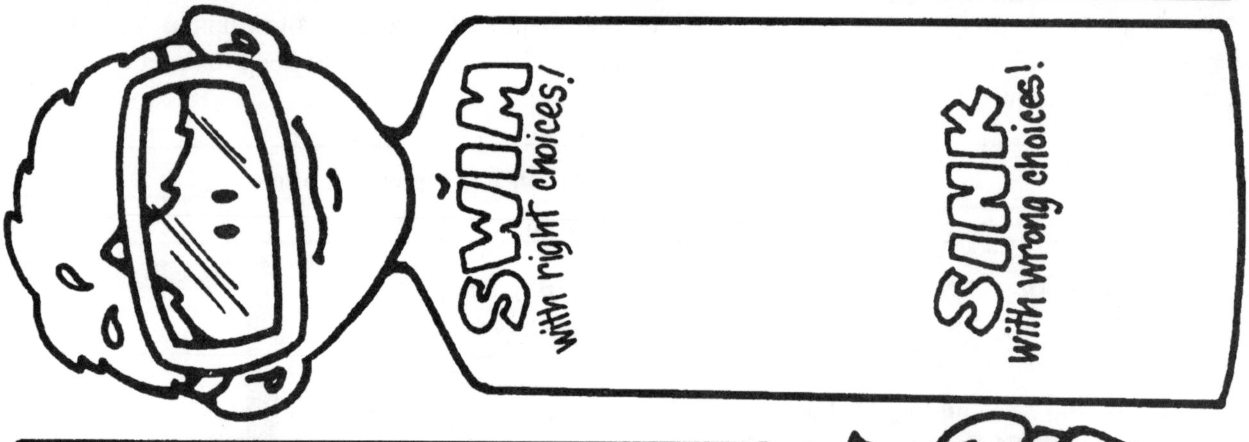

PATTERN: *COVENANTS (Sink or Swim wordstrips)*

1. OBEY GOD'S COMMANDMENTS. SINK OR SWIM?	12. ATTEND PRIMARY AND SACRAMENT MEETING. SINK OR SWIM?
2. SWEAR. SINK OR SWIM?	13. PRAY. SINK OR SWIM?
3. SMOKE CIGARETTES. SINK OR SWIM?	14. BE REVERENT. SINK OR SWIM?
4. READ THE SCRIPTURES. SINK OR SWIM?	15. FORGET TO PRAY. SINK OR SWIM?
5. COPY A FRIEND'S HOMEWORK. SINK OR SWIM?	16. BORROW SOMETHING AND NOT RETURN IT. SINK OR SWIM?
6. HONOR PARENTS. SINK OR SWIM?	17. CHEER UP THE SICK AND ELDERLY. SINK OR SWIM?
7. TELL A LIE. SINK OR SWIM?	18. DON'T ASK YOUR PARENTS WHAT YOU CAN DO TO HELP. SINK OR SWIM?
8. HELP OTHERS. SINK OR SWIM?	19. READ THE BOOK OF MORMON. SINK OR SWIM?
9. DON'T TALK TO LONELY OR SHY KIDS AT SCHOOL. SINK OR SWIM?	20. BRING A FRIEND TO CHURCH. SINK OR SWIM?
10. READ BOOKS THAT DON'T GIVE YOU A GOOD FEELING. SINK OR SWIM?	21. WALK AWAY FROM SHOWS THAT DON'T INVITE THE SPIRIT. SINK OR SWIM?
11. SPEND YOUR TITHING MONEY. SINK OR SWIM?	22. DON'T SHARE YOUR TESTIMONY. SINK OR SWIM?

PORTRAIT OF MY SPIRITUAL HERO

TRAITS TO FOLLOW:

____

____

____

____

*Lesson #27** HOLY GHOST: Jesus Speaks to Me Through the Holy Ghost

(Find the Spirit of Truth cross match)

YOU'LL NEED: Copy of Scripture Challenge card (page 106) on colored cardstock paper and Spirit of Truth cross match (page 50) for each child, pencils, and crayons or markers.

Review Enrichment Activity #2 (page 119) in Primary 6 Old Testament manual.*

ACTIVITIES: Help children know the difference between righteous ideas (IDEAS FROM GOD) and unrighteous ideas (IDEAS NOT FROM GOD). Explain that ideas are like a light going on inside our mind. The light that comes FROM GOD is a bright light that brings a warm happy feeling. The light that comes NOT FROM GOD is a dim light that brings a cold, sad feeling. See Spirit of Truth cross match.

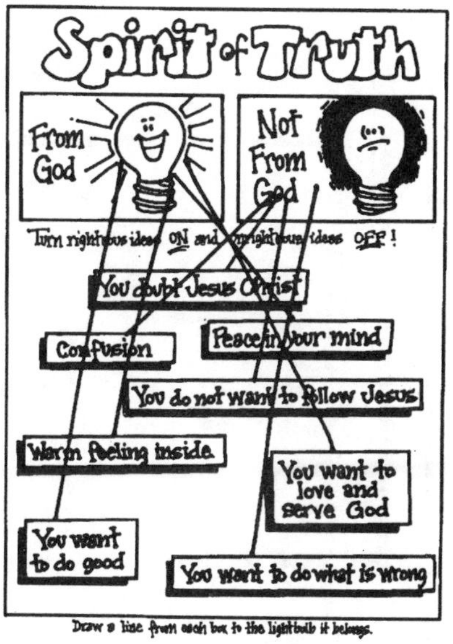

ANSWERS AND ADDITIONAL SCRIPTURE READING:
IDEAS FROM GOD: D&C 9:8 (warm feeling inside), Moroni 7:13 (you want to do good), Moroni 7:13 (you want to love and serve God), D&C 6:23 and John 14:27 (peace in your mind)
IDEAS NOT FROM GOD: D&C 9:9 (confusion), Moroni 7:17 (you want to do wrong, you do not want to follow Jesus, you doubt Jesus Christ)

SCRIPTURE CHALLENGE: Do activity in class or at home.

THOUGHT TREAT: Smile and Frown Cookie. Frost two small round cookies for each child (one with a smile and the other with a frown). As children eat the smile cookie, talk about the feelings that come when ideas are FROM GOD. While eating the frown cookie, talk about the feelings that come when ideas are NOT FROM GOD.

*Lesson #28** PRAYER: Heavenly Father Helps Me as I Pray in Faith

(My Personal Goliaths prayer journal)

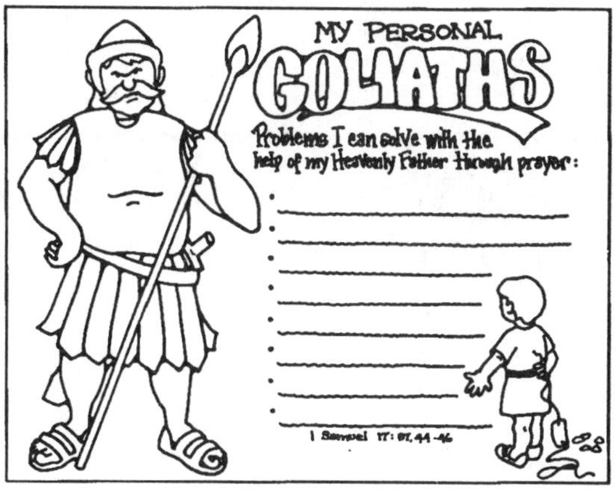

YOU'LL NEED: Copy of Scripture Challenge card (page 106) on cardstock paper, and My Personal Goliaths prayer journal (page 51) for each child, pencils, and markers.

Review Enrichment Activities #2, 3, and 4 (page 122) in Primary 6 Old Testament manual.*

ACTIVITY: Talk about the courage David had to fight Goliath. Read: 1 Samuel 17:37 and 17:44-46. Help children write problems they can solve with the help of Heavenly Father through prayer (1 Samuel 17:37).
EXAMPLES: School, family, friends, not having friends, feeling alone, other children making fun of them, not being able to talk to someone, not enough money.

SCRIPTURE CHALLENGE: Do activity in class or at home.

THOUGHT TREAT: David's Sling Licorice String. Tie string licorice or licorice rope like a sling shot (with a knot at one end to hold a stone). Eat licorice, talk about the courage David had to fight, knowing he had the power of God to help him. Read 1 Samuel 17:49-50.

Primary 6 manual is published by The Church of Jesus Christ of Latter-day Saints, Salt Lake City, Utah.

Spirit of Truth

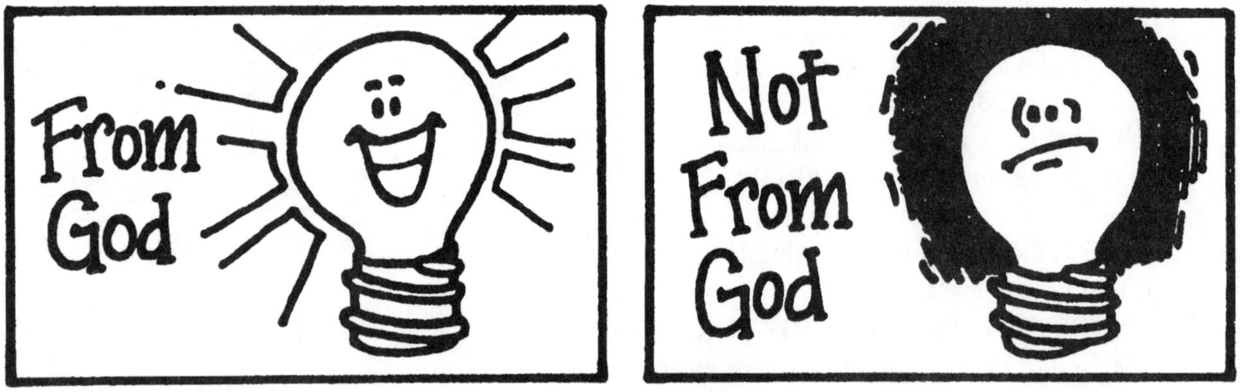

Turn righteous ideas ON and unrighteous ideas OFF!

You doubt Jesus Christ

Confusion

Peace in your mind

You do not want to follow Jesus

Warm feeling inside

You want to love and serve God

You want to do good

You want to do what is wrong

Draw a line from each box to the lightbulb it belongs to.

MY PERSONAL GOLIATHS

Problems I can solve with the help of my Heavenly Father through prayer:

- ______________________________
- ______________________________
- ______________________________
- ______________________________
- ______________________________
- ______________________________
- ______________________________
- ______________________________

1 Samuel 17: 37, 44-46

*Lesson #29**

FRIENDSHIP: I Can Be a True Friend to Jesus and Others

(Fishing for a Friend spin-and-tell)

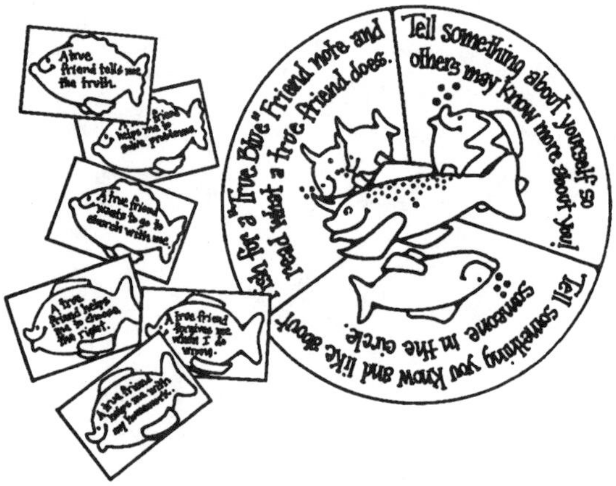

YOU'LL NEED: Copy of Scripture Challenge card (page 107) and spin-and-tell spinner and "true blue" friend notes (pages 53-54) on colored cardstock paper for each child, scissors, metal or button brad, and crayons or markers.

ACTIVITY: Help children learn the qualities of a "true blue" friend. (1) Color and cut out circle and fish spinner. (2) Attach fish to circle center with a metal or button brad. To make a button brad: Sew two buttons together on opposite sides, threading thread through the same holes) to attach fish to circle.

Review Attention Activity (page 125) and Enrichment Activities #2 and 4 (page 128) in Primary 6 Old Testament manual.*

TO PLAY FISHING FOR A FRIEND SPIN-AND-TELL: Sit in a circle and take turns spinning the fish. Do one of the three things: (1) Tell something about yourself so others may know more about you. (2) Tell something you know and like about someone in the circle. (3) Fish for a "true blue" friend note and read what a true friend does. ("True blue" friend notes should be placed face down in the center to draw from.)

SCRIPTURE CHALLENGE: Do activity in class or at home.

THOUGHT TREAT: Friendship Fish. Purchase fish-shaped crackers or gummy candy. As children eat, ask them to name qualities they would like in a friend. Talk about how Jonathan helped David (1 Samuel 23:16-17).

*Lesson #30**

CHOOSE THE RIGHT: I Will Keep My Thoughts and Actions Pure

(Mind Power wheel)

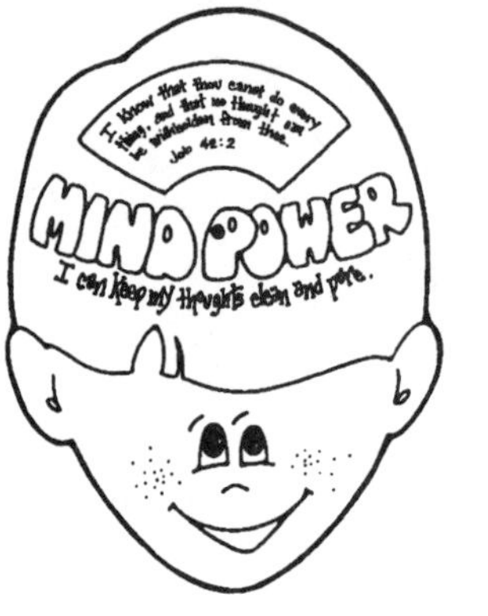

YOU'LL NEED: Copy of Scripture Challenge card (page 107) and Mind Power wheel parts A and B (pages 55-56) on colored cardstock paper, for each child, scissors, metal or button brad, and crayons.

ACTIVITY: Tell children that with this Mind Power wheel they can learn to develop "wheelie" good thoughts. (1) Color and cut out parts A and B. Cut hair off around face for boys and leave hair on for girls. Cut window out at the top of the head. (2) Attach wheel on the back of head by placing a metal or button brad through the center dots. To make a button brad: Sew two buttons together on opposite sides (threading thread through the same holes) to attach head to wheel. (3) Ask children to take turns turning the wheel and reading the scripture that tells them how to keep their thoughts clean and pure. **SCRIPTURE CHALLENGE:** Do activity in class or at home.

Review Enrichment Activity #3 (page 133) in Primary 6 Old Testament manual.*

THOUGHT TREAT: Sweet and Sour "Thought" Treats. Share and compare frosted cupcakes with the gospel of Jesus Christ that is so sweet, and sour pickles with the bitterness that comes from thoughts and actions that are not pure. Tell children that their thoughts grow sweeter as they learn about the gospel and choose the right. OPTION: Frost CTR on cupcakes.

Primary 6 manual is published by The Church of Jesus Christ of Latter-day Saints, Salt Lake City, Utah.

PATTERN: *FRIENDSHIP (Fishing for a Friend spin-and-tell)*

PATTERN: *FRIENDSHIP (Fishing for a Friend spin-and-tell)*

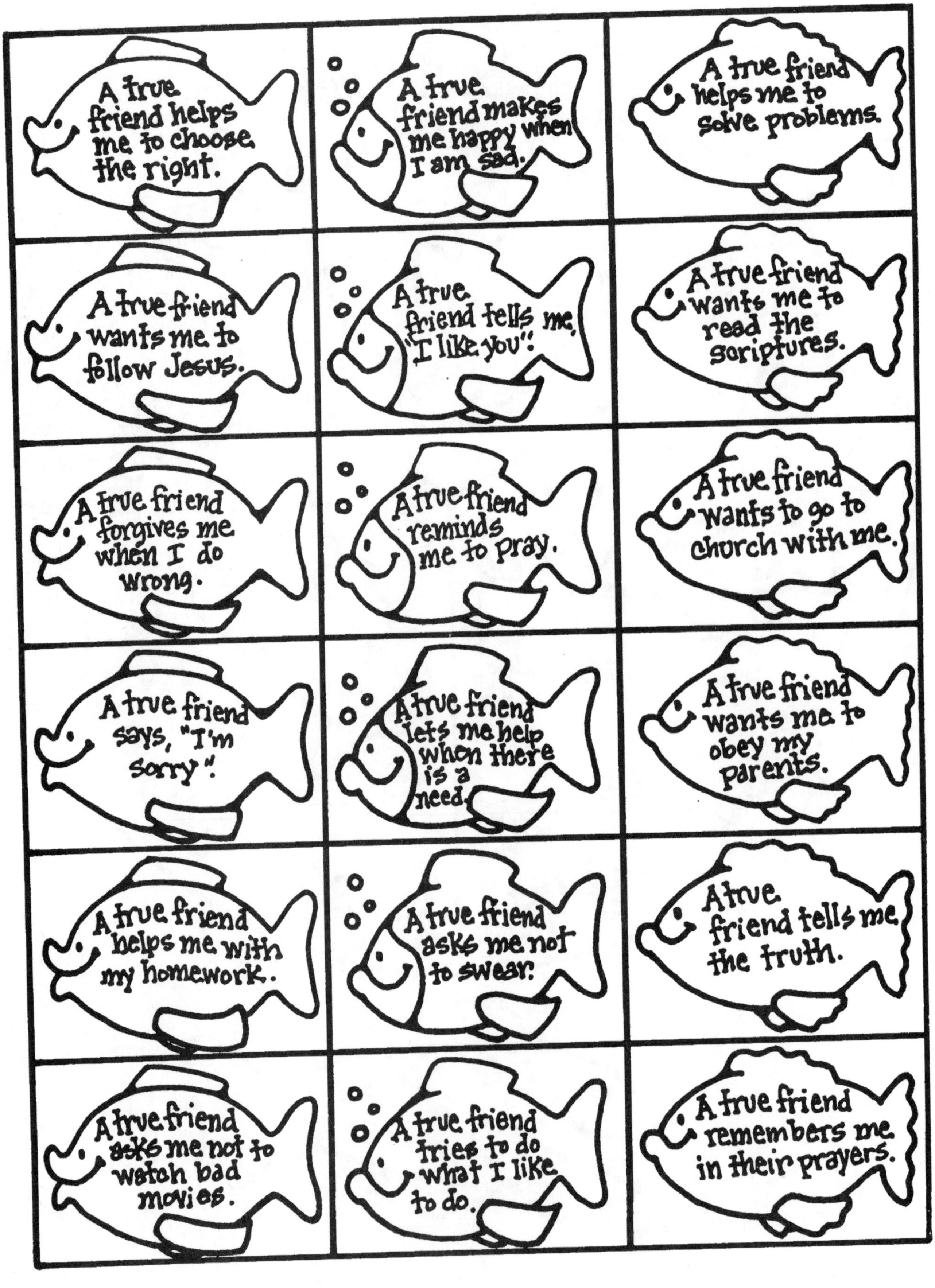

A true friend helps me to choose the right.
A true friend makes me happy when I am sad.
A true friend helps me to solve problems.
A true friend wants me to follow Jesus.
A true friend tells me, "I like you".
A true friend wants me to read the scriptures.
A true friend forgives me when I do wrong.
A true friend reminds me to pray.
A true friend wants to go to church with me.
A true friend says, "I'm sorry".
A true friend lets me help when there is a need.
A true friend wants me to obey my parents.
A true friend helps me with my homework.
A true friend asks me not to swear.
A true friend tells me the truth.
A true friend asks me not to watch bad movies.
A true friend tries to do what I like to do.
A true friend remembers me in their prayers.

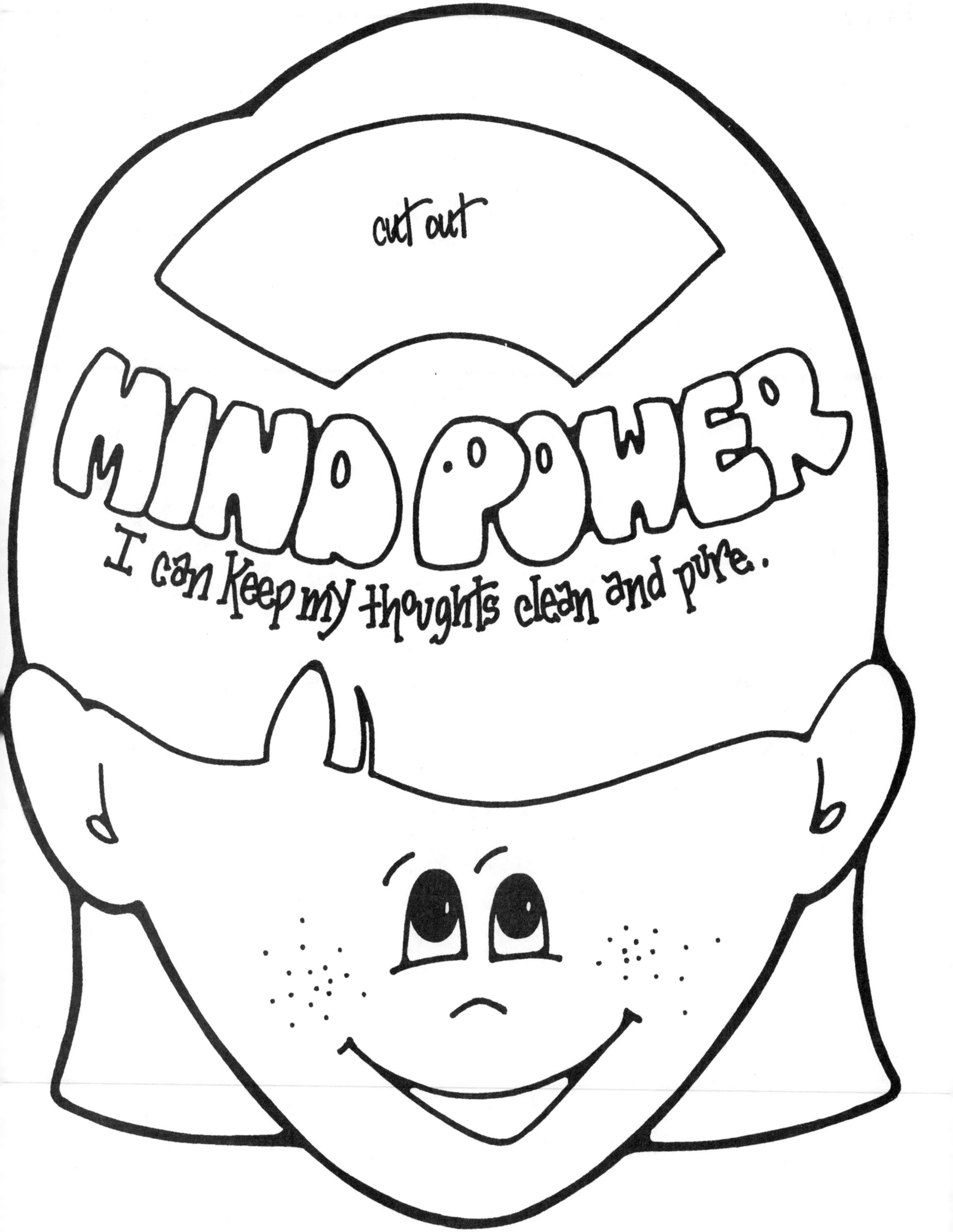
cut out
MIND POWER
I can keep my thoughts clean and pure.

PATTERN: *CHOOSE THE RIGHT (Mind Power "wheelie" good thoughts wheel)*

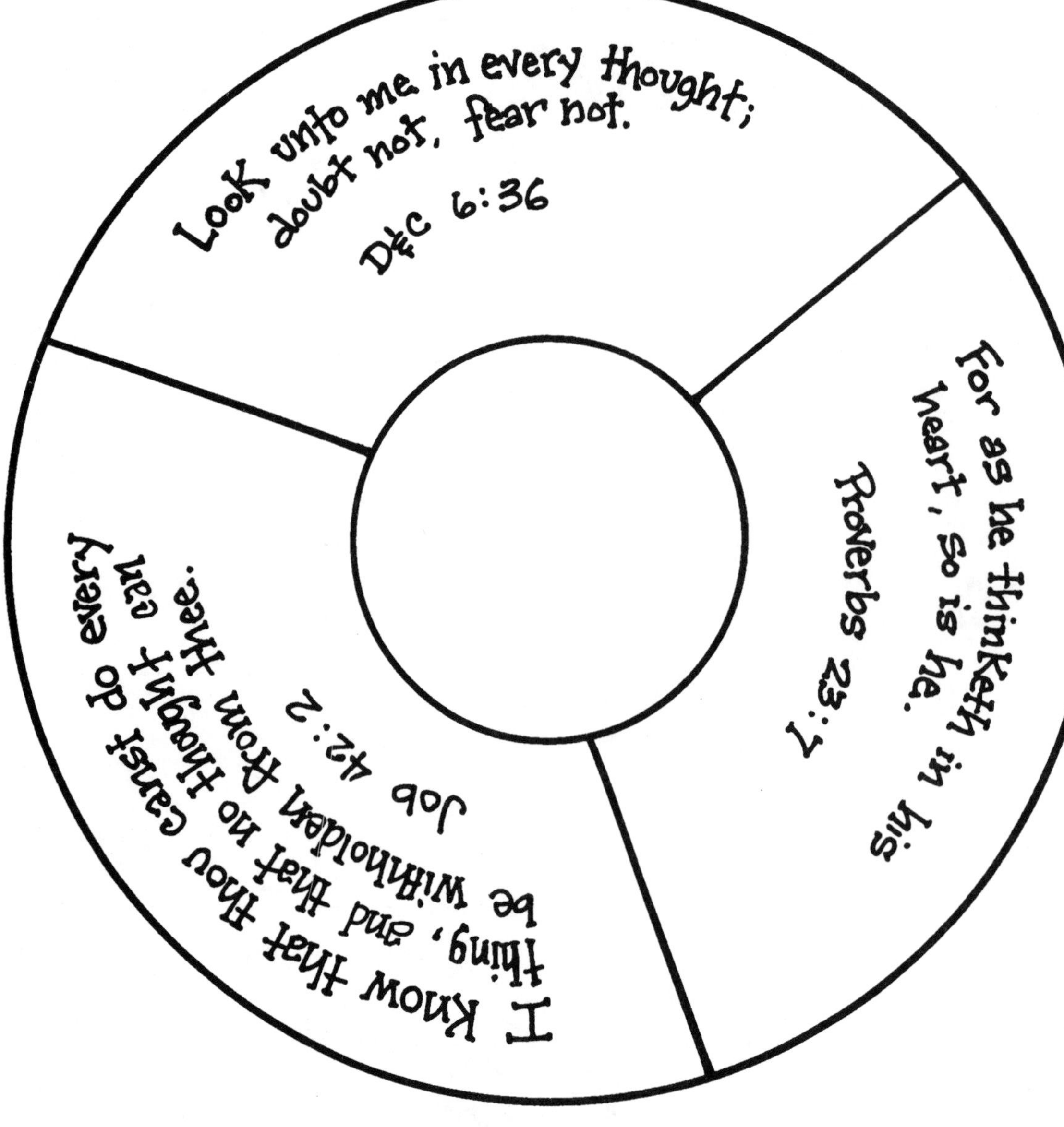

*Lesson #31** WISDOM: I Seek Wisdom, Knowledge, and an Understanding Heart

(Heavenly Treasures sack)

YOU'LL NEED: Copy of Scripture Challenge card (pages 108) and My Heavenly Treasures Sack label (page 58) on colored cardstock paper, wisdom wordstrips (pages 59-60) for each child, scissors, zip-close plastic sandwich bags, and crayons or markers.

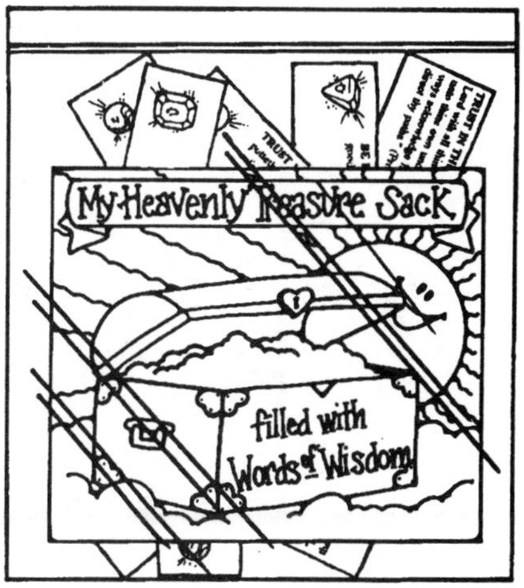

Review Enrichment Activity #4 (page 138) in Primary 6 Old Testament manual.*

ACTIVITIES: Children can take home words of wisdom in a Heavenly Treasures sack. They can read a scripture each day to remind them of the treasures that are of lasting worth.

1. Color and cut out label and wisdom wordstrips.
2. Take turns reading wordstrips and talking about the words of wisdom found in the scriptures.

SCRIPTURE CHALLENGE: Do activity in class or at home.

THOUGHT TREAT: Heavenly Treasure Wisdom Waffles. Butter waffles ahead of time and sprinkle cinnamon and sugar mixture (3/4 sugar 1/4 cinnamon) on top. Broil 2 minutes in the oven to melt butter and cinnamon sugar mixture onto waffle. Serve waffles cold. Tell children that heaven is sweet. Each groove in the waffle can represent a heavenly treasure you can take with you such as: wisdom, knowledge, an understanding heart, prayer, scripture study, testimony, good deeds, baptism, right choices. Encourage children to dig deep into the scriptures each day to find heavenly treasures.

*Lesson #32** PEER PRESSURE: I Will Be a Positive Influence on My Friends

(Peer Pressure cross match puzzle)

YOU'LL NEED: Copy of Scripture Challenge card (page 108) and Peer Pressure cross match puzzle (page 61) on colored cardstock paper for each child, pencils, and crayons or markers.

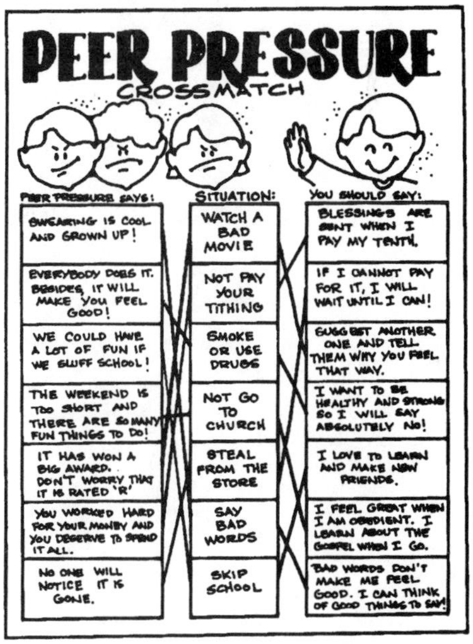

PEER PRESSURE
CROSSMATCH
PEER PRESSURE SAYS:
SITUATION:
YOU SHOULD SAY:
SWEARING IS COOL AND GROWN UP!
EVERYBODY DOES IT. BESIDES, IT WILL MAKE YOU FEEL GOOD!
WE COULD HAVE A LOT OF FUN IF WE SLUFF SCHOOL!
THE WEEKEND IS TOO SHORT AND THERE ARE SO MANY FUN THINGS TO DO!
IT HAS WON A BIG AWARD. DON'T WORRY THAT IT IS RATED 'R'
YOU WORKED HARD FOR YOUR MONEY AND YOU DESERVE TO SPEND IT ALL.
NO ONE WILL NOTICE IT IS GONE.
WATCH A BAD MOVIE
NOT PAY YOUR TITHING
SMOKE OR USE DRUGS
NOT GO TO CHURCH
STEAL FROM THE STORE
SAY BAD WORDS
SKIP SCHOOL
BLESSINGS ARE SENT WHEN I PAY MY TENTH.
IF I CANNOT PAY FOR IT, I WILL WAIT UNTIL I CAN!
SUGGEST ANOTHER ONE AND TELL THEM WHY YOU FEEL THAT WAY.
I WANT TO BE HEALTHY AND STRONG SO I WILL SAY ABSOLUTELY NO!
I LOVE TO LEARN AND MAKE NEW FRIENDS.
I FEEL GREAT WHEN I AM OBEDIENT. I LEARN ABOUT THE GOSPEL WHEN I GO.
BAD WORDS DON'T MAKE ME FEEL GOOD. I CAN THINK OF GOOD THINGS TO SAY!

Review Enrichment Activity #1 (page 142) in Primary 6 Old Testament manual.*

ACTIVITY: Help children learn how to respond to pressure situations, to be a positive influence on their friends.

HOW: Draw an arrow from the pressure situation (listed in the center column) to the left (negative peer pressure). Then draw an arrow from the pressure situation to the right (your positive influence). Talk about the consequences for each decision. **OPTION:** Use different colors to draw arrows.

SCRIPTURE CHALLENGE: Do activity in class or at home.

THOUGHT TREAT: Peer Pressure Pop. Open a can of pop and talk about the pressure that comes as you lift the lid. Talk about peer pressure as you pour each child some pop in a small cup. Tell children a similar pressure (to this can of pop opening) is felt when friends suggest you do something that is wrong. You feel uneasy and restless. You can ease this pressure if you know your values (what you believe in). You know what is right and you can say 'no.' This way you can be a positive influence to others.

Primary 6 manual is published by The Church of Jesus Christ of Latter-day Saints, Salt Lake City, Utah.

PATTERN: *WISDOM (Words of Wisdom Heavenly Treasure sack)*

PATTERN: *WISDOM (Heavenly Treasures sack wisdom wordstrips)*

OBEY PARENTS: "Hear the instruction of thy father, and forsake not the law of thy mother." (Proverbs 1:8)

SAY "NO" TO TEMPTATION: "If sinners entice thee, consent thou not." (Proverbs 1:10)

TRUST IN THE LORD: "Trust in the Lord with all thine heart; and lean not unto thine own understanding. In all thy ways acknowledge him, and he shall direct thy paths." (Proverbs 3:5-6)

FIND WISDOM AND UNDERSTANDING: "Happy is the man that findeth wisdom, and the man that getteth understanding." (Proverbs 3:13)

TELL THE TRUTH: "Lying lips are an abomination to the Lord: but they that deal truly are his delight." (Proverbs 12:22)

AVOID LOUD SPEECH: "A soft answer turneth away wrath." (Proverbs 15:1)

BE HAPPY AND SMILE: "A merry heart maketh a cheerful countenance." (Proverbs 15:13)

LIVE SO PRAYERS ARE HEARD: "The Lord is far from the wicked: but he heareth the prayer of the righteous." (Proverbs 15:29)

SEEK WISDOM TREASURES: "How much better is it to get wisdom than gold!" (Proverbs 16:16)

BE HUMBLE: "Pride goeth before destruction, and an haughty spirit before a fall." (Proverbs 16:18)

SPEAK KIND WORDS: "Pleasant words are as an honeycomb, sweet to the soul, and health to the bones." (Proverbs 16:24)

LOVE OTHERS: "A friend loveth at all times." (Proverbs 17:17)

BE HAPPY: "A merry heart doeth good like a medicine." (Proverbs 17:22)

DON'T DRINK ALCOHOLIC BEVERAGES: "Wine is a mocker, strong drink is raging: and whosoever is deceived thereby is not wise." (Proverbs 20:1)

BE RIGHTEOUS: "Even a child is known by his doings, whether his work be pure, and whether it be right." (Proverbs 20:11)

THINK RIGHTEOUS THOUGHTS: "As he thinketh in his heart, so is he." (Proverbs 23:7)

BE FAITHFUL TO OBTAIN BLESSINGS: "A faithful man shall abound with blessings." (Proverbs 28:20)

TRUST IN THE LORD: "Whoso putteth his trust in the Lord shall be safe." (Proverbs 29:25)

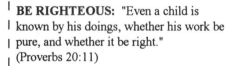

PATTERN: *WISDOM (Heavenly Treasures sack wisdom wordstrips)*

TESTIMONY: "Except ye become converted, and become as little children, ye shall not enter into the kingdom of heaven." (Matthew 18:3)

STRAIT GATE: "Strive to enter in at the strait gate: for many, I say unto you, will seek to enter in, and shall not be able." (Luke 13:24)

CHOOSE THE RIGHT: "If ye know these things, happy are ye if ye do them." (John 13:17)

KEEP TRYING: "Behold, we count them happy which endure." (James 5:11)

STUDY SCRIPTURES: "They received the word with readiness of mind, and searched the scriptures daily." (Acts 17:11) "Study . . . the word of truth." (2 Timothy 2:15)

KEEP COMMANDMENTS: "For this is the love of God, that we keep his commandments." (1 John 5:3)

GET WISDOM: "The holy scriptures . . . are able to make thee wise unto salvation through faith which is in Christ Jesus. All scripture is given by inspiration of God, . . . for instruction in righteousness: That the man of God be perfect." (2 Timothy 3:15-17)

LOVE: "If a man say, I love God, and hateth his brother, he is a liar: for he that loveth not his brother whom he hath seen, how can he love God whom he hath not seen?" (1 John 4:20)

SCRIPTURES TELL OF JESUS: "Search the scriptures; for in them ye think ye have eternal life; and they are they which testify of me." (John 5:39)

LOVE: "A new commandment I give unto you, That ye love one another; as I have loved you, that ye also love one another." (John 13:34)

PRAYER: "Your Father [in Heaven] knoweth what things ye have need of, before ye ask him." (Matthew 6:8)

BELIEVE IN JESUS: "I am come a light into the world, that whosoever believeth on me should not abide in darkness." (John 12:46)

TESTIMONY: "Wherefore I give you to understand, that no man . . . can say that Jesus is the Lord, but by the Holy Ghost." (1 Corinthians 12:3)

CHOOSE THE RIGHT: "Be ye therefore perfect, even as your Father which is in heaven is perfect." (Matthew 5:48)

PRAYER: "When thou prayest, enter into thy closet, and when thou hast shut thy door, pray to thy Father which is in secret; and thy Father which seeth in secret shall reward thee openly." (Matthew 6:6)

LET YOUR LIGHT SHINE: "Ye are the light of the world . . . Let your light so shine before men, that they may see your good works, and glorify your Father which is in heaven." (Matthew 5:14-16)

SEEK HEAVEN: "Seek ye first the kingdom of God, and his righteousness; and all these things shall be added unto you." (Matthew 6:33)

BELIEVE & BE BAPTIZED: "He that believeth and is baptized shall be saved; but he that believeth not shall be damned." (Mark 16:16)

PATTERN: ***WISDOM (Heavenly Treasures sack wisdom wordstrips)***

HEAVEN: "Not every one that saith unto me, Lord, Lord, shall enter into the kingdom of heaven; but he that doeth the will of my Father which is in heaven." (Matthew 7:21)

JESUS IS HEAVEN SENT: "And no man hath ascended up to heaven, but he that came down from heaven, even the Son of man which is in heaven." (John 3:13)

HEAVEN: "He that endureth to the end shall be saved." (Matthew 10:22)

SCRIPTURE WARNING: "Jesus answered and said unto them, Ye do err, not knowing the scriptures, nor the power of God." (Matthew 22:29)

TREASURES ON EARTH AND HEAVEN: "Jesus . . . saith unto them, Children, how hard is it for them that trust in riches to enter into the kingdom of God! It is easier for a camel to go through the eye of a needle, than for a rich man to enter into the kingdom of God." (Mark 10:24-25)

TWO GREAT COMMANDMENTS: "Jesus said unto him, Thou shalt love the Lord thy God with all thy heart, and with all thy soul, and with all thy mind. This is the first and great commandment. And the second is like unto it, Thou shalt love thy neighbour as thyself." (Matthew 22:37-39)

BELIEVE IN JESUS: "He that believeth on the Son hath everlasting life: and he that believeth not the Son shall not see life; but the wrath of God abideth on him." (John 3:36)

HEAVEN BOUND: "Verily I say unto you, Whatsoever ye shall bind on earth shall be bound in heaven: and whatsoever ye shall loose on earth shall be loosed in heaven." (Matthew 18:18)

CHILDREN: "Jesus . . . said unto them, Suffer the little children to come unto me, and forbid them not: for of such is the kingdom of God." (Mark 10:14)

ETERNAL LIFE: "And this is life eternal, that they might know thee the only true God, and Jesus Christ, whom thou hast sent." (John 17:3)

FAITH: "If I have told you earthly things, and ye believe not, how shall ye believe, if I tell you heavenly things?" (John 3:12)

STRENGTH: "Put on the whole armour of God, that ye may be able to stand against the wiles of the devil." (Ephesians 6:11)

FAITH & WORKS: "Faith, if it hath not works, is dead." (James 2:17)

COMMANDMENTS: "If ye love me, keep my commandments." (John 14:15)

TRUTH: "Know the truth, and the truth shall make you free." (John 8:32)

DOING GOOD: "If ye know these things, happy are ye if ye do them." (John 13:17)

PEER PRESSURE

CROSSMATCH

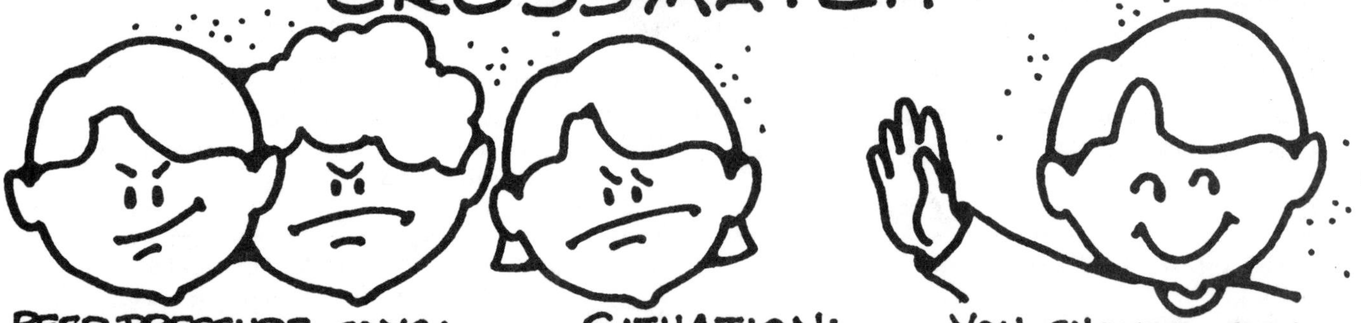

PEER PRESSURE SAYS:	SITUATION:	YOU SHOULD SAY:
SWEARING IS COOL AND GROWN UP!	WATCH A BAD MOVIE	BLESSINGS ARE SENT WHEN I PAY MY TENTH.
EVERYBODY DOES IT. BESIDES, IT WILL MAKE YOU FEEL GOOD!	NOT PAY YOUR TITHING	IF I CANNOT PAY FOR IT, I WILL WAIT UNTIL I CAN!
WE COULD HAVE A LOT OF FUN IF WE SLUFF SCHOOL!	SMOKE OR USE DRUGS	SUGGEST ANOTHER ONE AND TELL THEM WHY YOU FEEL THAT WAY.
THE WEEKEND IS TOO SHORT AND THERE ARE SO MANY FUN THINGS TO DO!	NOT GO TO CHURCH	I WANT TO BE HEALTHY AND STRONG SO I WILL SAY ABSOLUTELY NO!
IT HAS WON A BIG AWARD. DON'T WORRY THAT IT IS RATED 'R'	STEAL FROM THE STORE	I LOVE TO LEARN AND MAKE NEW FRIENDS.
YOU WORKED HARD FOR YOUR MONEY AND YOU DESERVE TO SPEND IT ALL.	SAY BAD WORDS	I FEEL GREAT WHEN I AM OBEDIENT. I LEARN ABOUT THE GOSPEL WHEN I GO.
NO ONE WILL NOTICE IT IS GONE.	SKIP SCHOOL	BAD WORDS DON'T MAKE ME FEEL GOOD. I CAN THINK OF GOOD THINGS TO SAY!

*Lesson #33** PRIESTHOOD: The Priesthood Blesses My Life

(Priesthood Pockets puzzle)

Review Enrichment Activity #1 (page 146) in Primary 6 Old Testament manual.*

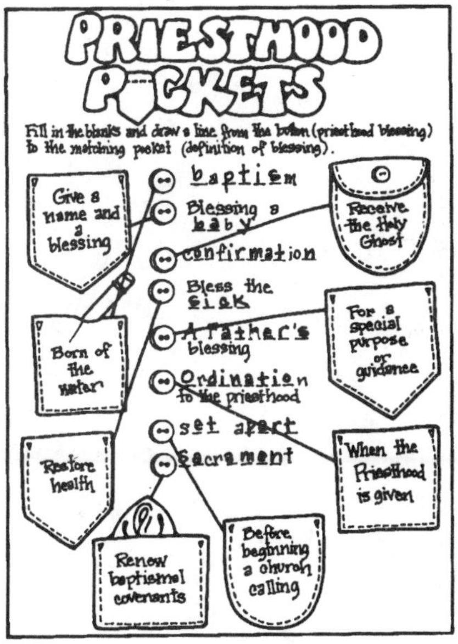

YOU'LL NEED: Copy of Scripture Challenge card (page 109) on colored cardstock paper and Priesthood Pockets puzzle (page 64) for each child, pencils, and crayons.

ACTIVITY: Help children learn how the priesthood power can bless their lives by matching the blessing with the definition. (1) Color and cut out puzzle. (2) Fill in the blanks and draw a line from the button to the matching pocket.

SCRIPTURE CHALLENGE: Do in class or at home.

THOUGHT TREAT: Priesthood Peanut Butter Cookies. Purchase peanut butter filled cookies or spread peanut butter between two graham crackers. Tell children that the priesthood is one half of the cookie and our faith is the other half. Priesthood blessings cannot come to us if we don't have faith. The peanut butter in the cookie reminds us to stick to beliefs. As we live the commandments each day, our faith increases, and we stay worthy to receive priesthood blessings.

*Lesson #34** WORSHIP: I Honor Heavenly Father, Jesus Christ, and the Holy Ghost

(Whom Do I Worship? word find)

Review Enrichment Activity #4 (page 152) in Primary 6 Old Testament manual.*

YOU'LL NEED: Copy of Scripture Challenge card (page 109) and word find puzzle (page 65) on colored cardstock paper for each child, pencils, and crayons or markers.

ACTIVITY: Read the quote from the Prophet Ezra Taft Benson (*Ensign*, May 1988, pg. 5): "God our Father, Jesus, our Elder Brother and our Redeemer, and the Holy Ghost, the Testator, are perfect. They know us best and love us most and will not leave one thing undone for our eternal welfare." They want us to return to them.

TO DO WORD FIND: (1) Help children review the roles and titles of the three members of the Godhead with this backwards word find puzzle. (2) Tell children that the clue words are along the sides, and with letters mixed-up. Turn them around and write them in to learn whom you worship. **ANSWERS:** Heavenly Father: (Father, spirits, plan, world, pray) Jesus Christ: (brother, sin, death, savior, created, example) Holy Ghost: (small voice, spirit, comforter, heart, mind)

SCRIPTURE CHALLENGE: Do activity in class at home.

THOUGHT TREAT: "W" Worship Cookie. Create a "W" shaped cookie out of rolled sugar cookie dough. Frost and top "W" with 3 candies. Tell children that the 3 pieces of candy represent the 3 personages in the godhead: Heavenly Father, Jesus Christ, and the Holy Ghost.

**Primary 6* manual is published by The Church of Jesus Christ of Latter-day Saints, Salt Lake City, Utah.

PRIESTHOOD POCKETS

Fill in the blanks and draw a line from the button (priesthood blessing) to the matching pocket (definition of blessing).

- __a_____m
- Blessing a ___b_
- c__f______io_
- Bless the _____
- A F______'_ blessing
- __r_______n to the priesthood
- S__ a____
- __cr____t

Give a name and a blessing

Receive the Holy Ghost

Born of the water

For a special purpose or guidance

Restore health

When the Priesthood is given

Renew baptismal covenants

Before beginning a church calling

I HONOR HEAVENLY FATHER, JESUS AND THE HOLY GHOST

Worship WORDFIND

He is the ________ of our ________. He presented the ______ of salvation in our premortal life. He directed the creation of the ________. He is the God to whom we ______.

He is our elder ________. He overcame ______ and ________ so we could return to Heavenly Father. He is our ________. He ________ the earth. He is our perfect ________.

He speaks to us through a still ______ ______. He is the ________ of truth. He is called the ________ and testifier. He speaks to our ________ and ______.

- RSPTII
- DMIN
- NALP
- RIVASO
- RORBHTE
- HTDAE
- ROMROFCTE

- PSRIITS
- DEARCET
- NIS
- VECOI
- REATH
- THAFER
- PARY

- PLXAEME
- MALSL
- LROWD

*Lesson #35** OBEDIENCE: I Will Obey Righteous Leaders

(Blessings Blockbuster game)

YOU'LL NEED: Copy of Scripture Challenge card (page 110) and Blessings Blockbuster block and blessing cards (pages 67-68) on colored cardstock paper for each child, scissors, glue, and crayons or markers.

ACTIVITY: Encourage children to share what they feel are blessings from obeying righteous leaders.

1. Color and cut out block and blessing cards.
2. Fold box and glue flaps inside box.

OPTION: Stuff with cotton. Glue top closed.

Review Testimony (page 157) in Primary 6 Old Testament manual.*

TO PLAY THE BLESSINGS BLOCKBUSTER GAME:

Step #1: Divide into two teams.

Step #2: Take turns rolling the block to a number or Blessings Blockbuster. Record number as points for your team or give your team 6 points if a blockbuster is rolled. Points are earned by doing as follows:

Step #3: Draw and read a blessing card. Then say how you would be blessed by obeying the action on the card.

SCRIPTURE CHALLENGE: Do activity in class or at home.

THOUGHT TREAT: Big "O" Obedience Doughnuts. Give each child a doughnut and tell them to think about the letter "O" in obedience and the first letters "do" in doughnut. To obey is to do what someone asks you to do. If you want to live a righteous life, obey or do as you are asked to do by righteous leaders.

OPTION: Use this as the treat suggested in the Attention Activity (page 154) in the *Primary 6* Old Testament manual* by placing treat in a box.

*Lesson #36** SECOND COMING: I Will Prepare by Living Righteously

(Millennium Match Game)

YOU'LL NEED: Copy of Scripture Challenge card (page 110) and Millennium Match Game bag label and two of each card (pages 69-70) on colored cardstock paper for each child, scissors, zip-close plastic sandwich bags, and crayons.

ACTIVITY: Play the Millennium Match Game to help children prepare for the second coming of Jesus Christ. Tell children that if they learn what is to happen and live righteously, they can look forward to the peace and joy that will come in the Millennium.

Review Enrichment Activities #1 and #4 (pages 160-161) in Primary 6 Old Testament manual.*

TO MAKE GAME: Color and cut out the bag label and a set of cards (two of each card). Store cards and label in a plastic bag.

TO PLAY: Divide into teams. Take turns turning cards over to make a match. When a player makes a match, look up a scripture reference on the card and read the scripture aloud.

SCRIPTURE CHALLENGE: Do activity in class or home.

THOUGHT TREAT: Millennium M&Ms. Share 10 M&M candies for each child and ask children to each name one of the 10 signs of the second coming of Jesus Christ and the millennium (on game cards).

*Primary 6 manual is published by The Church of Jesus Christ of Latter-day Saints, Salt Lake City, Utah.

PATTERN: *OBEDIENCE (Blessings Blockbuster Game)*

PATTERN: *OBEDIENCE (Blessing Blockbuster Game cards)*

BLESSINGS FROM:
Emptying the garbage on time or cleaning my room.

BLESSINGS FROM:
Having personal and family prayer daily.

BLESSINGS FROM:
Reading the prophet's message in the Church magazines.

BLESSINGS FROM:
Attending church meetings.

BLESSINGS FROM:
Obeying my parents.

BLESSINGS FROM:
Serving or helping others.

BLESSINGS FROM:
Reading the scriptures daily.

BLESSINGS FROM:
Doing chores around the house or weeding garden without being asked.

BLESSINGS FROM:
Paying a full tithing.

BLESSINGS FROM:
Being honest.

BLESSINGS FROM:
Fasting and paying extra money for fast offerings.

BLESSINGS FROM:
Reading uplifting books, watching uplifting movies.

BLESSINGS FROM:
Planting a garden.

BLESSINGS FROM:
Being reverent during Primary and sacrament meeting.

Millennium Match

"Prepare ye, prepare ye for that which is to come, for the Lord is nigh." D&C 1:12

LAMANITES BECOME A MIGHTY PEOPLE

D&C 49:24

WICKEDNESS, WARS, TURMOIL

D&C 43:33-35
D&C 45: 26-27, 29, 31, 33, 42
ISAIAH 54:10, 13-14, 17

JESUS CHRIST WILL COME

D&C 45: 38-39, 44-46, 48-63
D&C 49: 27-28 D&C 29:11
10th ARTICLE OF FAITH

BUILDING OF THE NEW JERUSALEM
1,000 YEARS OF PEACE

D&C 45:16-25, 58-59, 65-71
D&C 29:11 JOHN 1:27
2 NEPHI 30:18

BIRTH OF JESUS CHRIST

ISAIAH 7:14

ATONEMENT OF JESUS CHRIST

ISAIAH 53:3-5

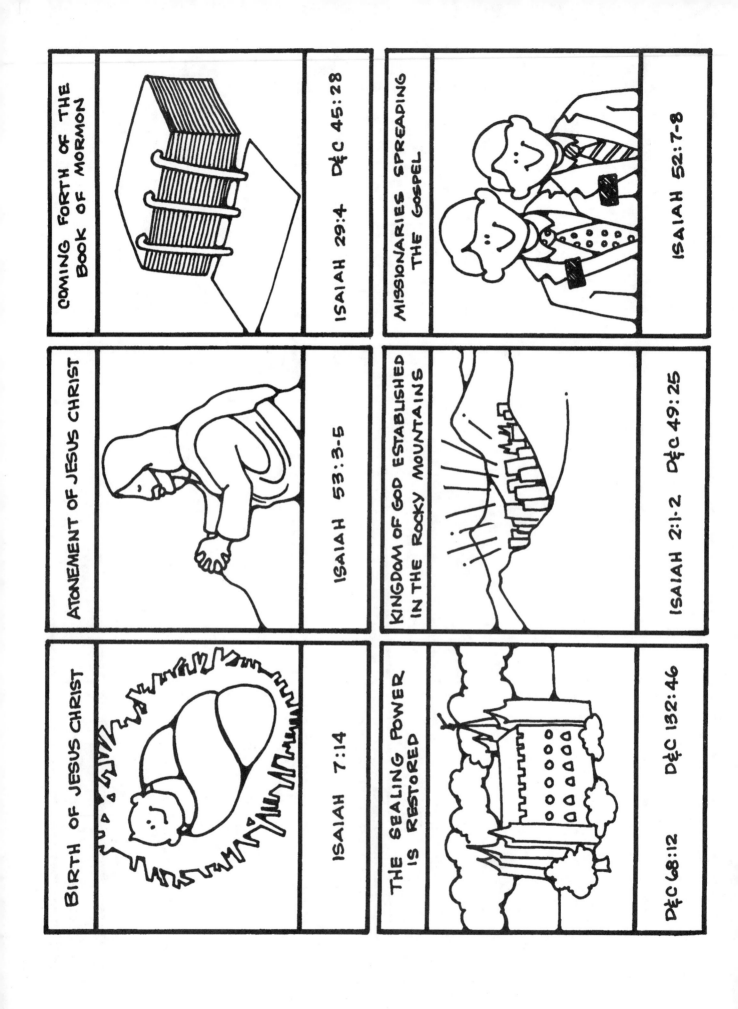

COMING FORTH OF THE BOOK OF MORMON

ISAIAH 29:4 D&C 45:28

THE SEALING POWER IS RESTORED

D&C 68:12 D&C 132:46

KINGDOM OF GOD ESTABLISHED IN THE ROCKY MOUNTAINS

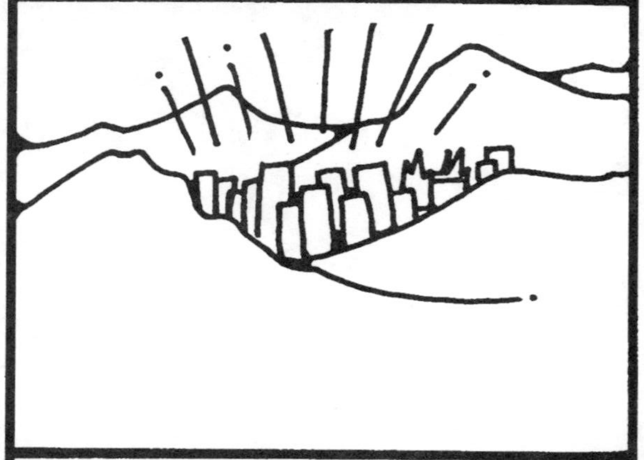

ISAIAH 2:1-2 D&C 49:25

MISSIONARIES SPREADING THE GOSPEL

ISAIAH 52:7-8

*Lesson #37** SCRIPTURES: I Will Be Blessed as I Read the Scriptures and Keep the Commandments *(sticker challenge)*

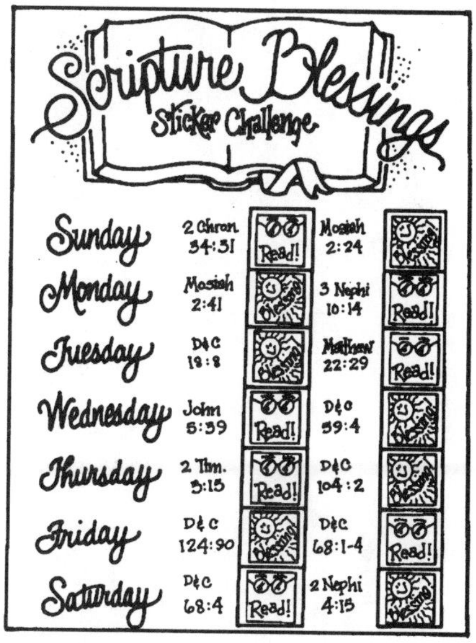

YOU'LL NEED: Copy of Scripture Challenge card (page 111) and Scripture Blessings sticker challenge and glue-on stickers (pages 72-73) on colored cardstock paper for each child, scissors, glue, and crayons or markers.

Review Testimony (page 166) in Primary 6 Old Testament manual.*

ACTIVITY: Help children discover the importance of reading the scriptures and the blessings that come from reading the scriptures and keeping the commandments. (1) Color chart and glue-on stickers. (2) Cut out glue-on stickers. (3) Read the two scriptures for each day starting with Sunday. (4) Decide which scripture tells you to "read" the scriptures and which scripture tells you the "blessings" that come from reading the scriptures and obeying the commandments. (5) Glue a "Read!" or a "Blessing!" sticker to the right of each scripture.

SCRIPTURE CHALLENGE: Do activity in class or at home.

THOUGHT TREAT: Standard Works Cookies. Break one four piece graham cracker into four pieces for each child. Frost between layers, stacking four cracker pieces together. Tell children that the scriptures consist of the four standard works: The Bible, Book of Mormon, Doctrine and Covenants, and Pearl of Great Price. Discuss how these differ from each other.

*Lesson #38** FASTING and Prayer Increase My Faith and Bring Blessings *(Fasting and Prayer Blessings puzzle)*

YOU'LL NEED: Copy of Scripture Challenge card (page 111) and Fasting and Prayer Brings Blessings puzzle (pages 74-75) on colored cardstock paper for each child, scissors, zip-close plastic sandwich bags, and crayons or markers.

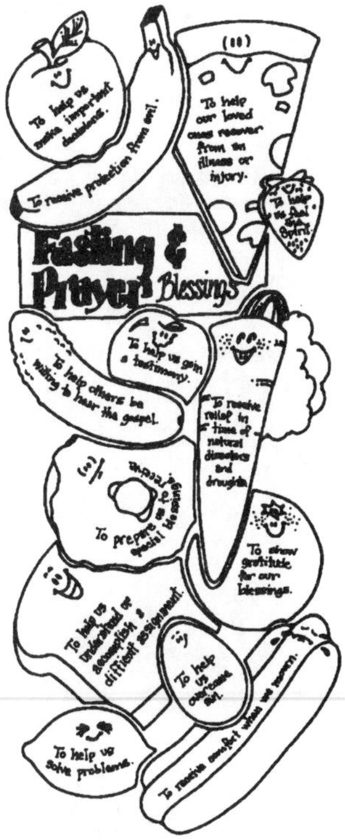

ACTIVITY: Challenge children to put together this food puzzle to learn of the blessings that come from fasting and prayer. Color and cut out puzzle (found on two pages) ahead of time and place in a zip-close plastic bag for each child.

Review Enrichment Activity #4 (pages 170-171) in Primary 6 Old Testament manual.*

SCRIPTURE CHALLENGE: Do activity in class or at home.

THOUGHT TREAT: Fasting and Prayer Yeast Bread. When the elements of yeast and sugar are put together, this helps bread to rise more quickly. When the elements of fasting and prayer are put together, they increase our faith. When our faith increases we become closer to Heavenly Father. Heavenly Father then blesses us and those for whom we fast and pray.

Review Attention Activity (page 167) in Primary 6 Old Testament manual.*

**Primary 6* manual is published by The Church of Jesus Christ of Latter-day Saints, Salt Lake City, Utah.

Scripture Blessings
Sticker Challenge

Sunday	2 Chron 34:31		Mosiah 2:24	
Monday	Mosiah 2:41		3 Nephi 10:14	
Tuesday	D&C 18:8		Matthew 22:29	
Wednesday	John 5:39		D&C 59:4	
Thursday	2 Tim. 3:15		D&C 104:2	
Friday	D&C 124:90		D&C 68:1-4	
Saturday	D&C 68:4		2 Nephi 4:15	

PATTERN: *SCRIPTURES (Scripture Blessings sticker challenge)*

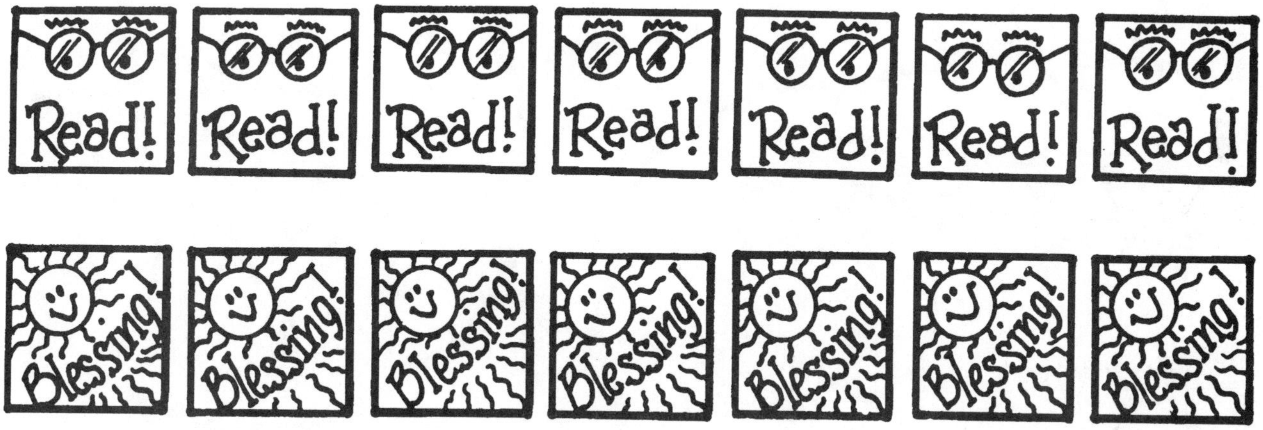

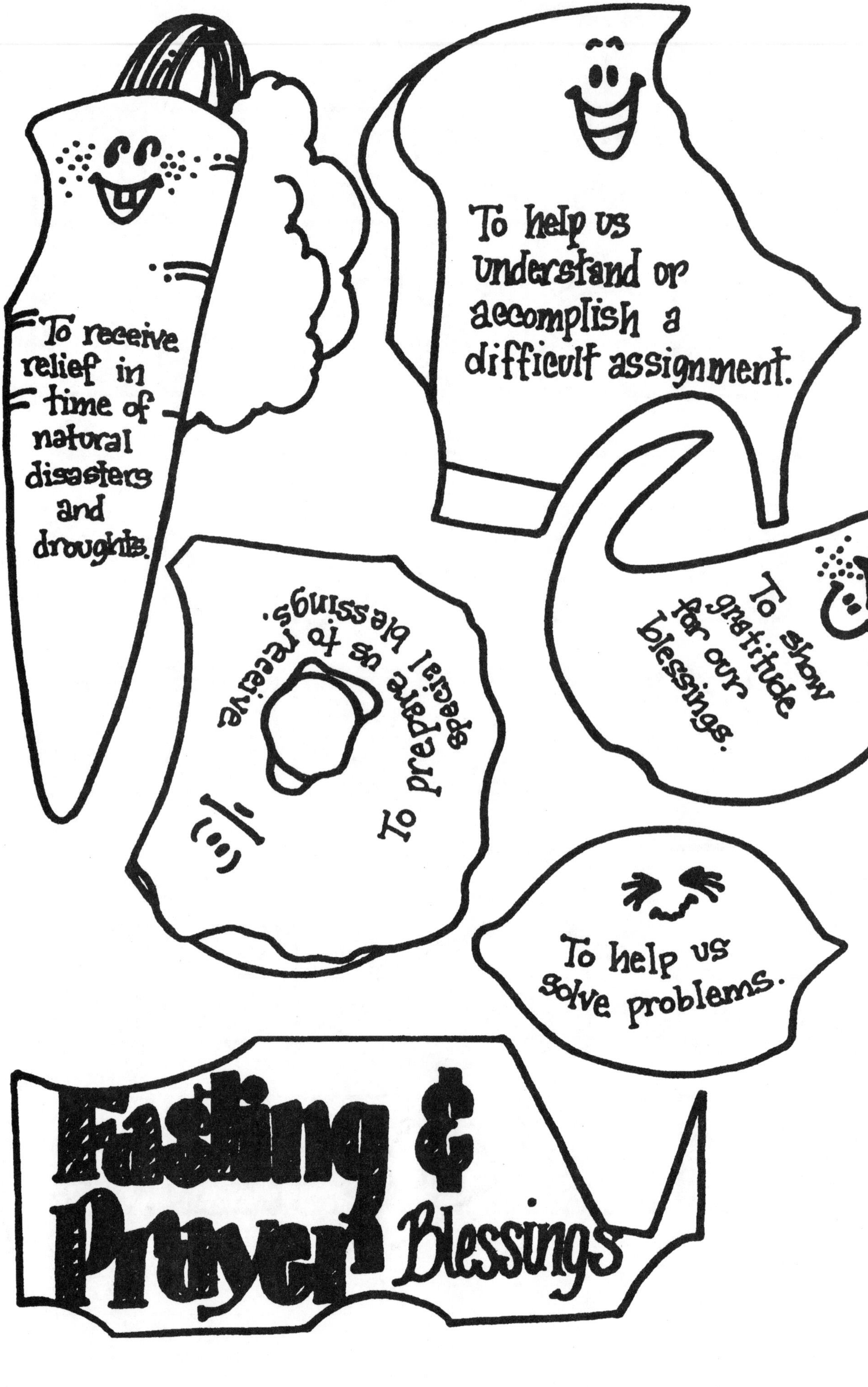
To receive relief in time of natural disasters and droughts.
To help us understand or accomplish a difficult assignment.
To show gratitude for our blessings.
To prepare us to receive special blessings.
To help us solve problems.
Fasting & Prayer Blessings

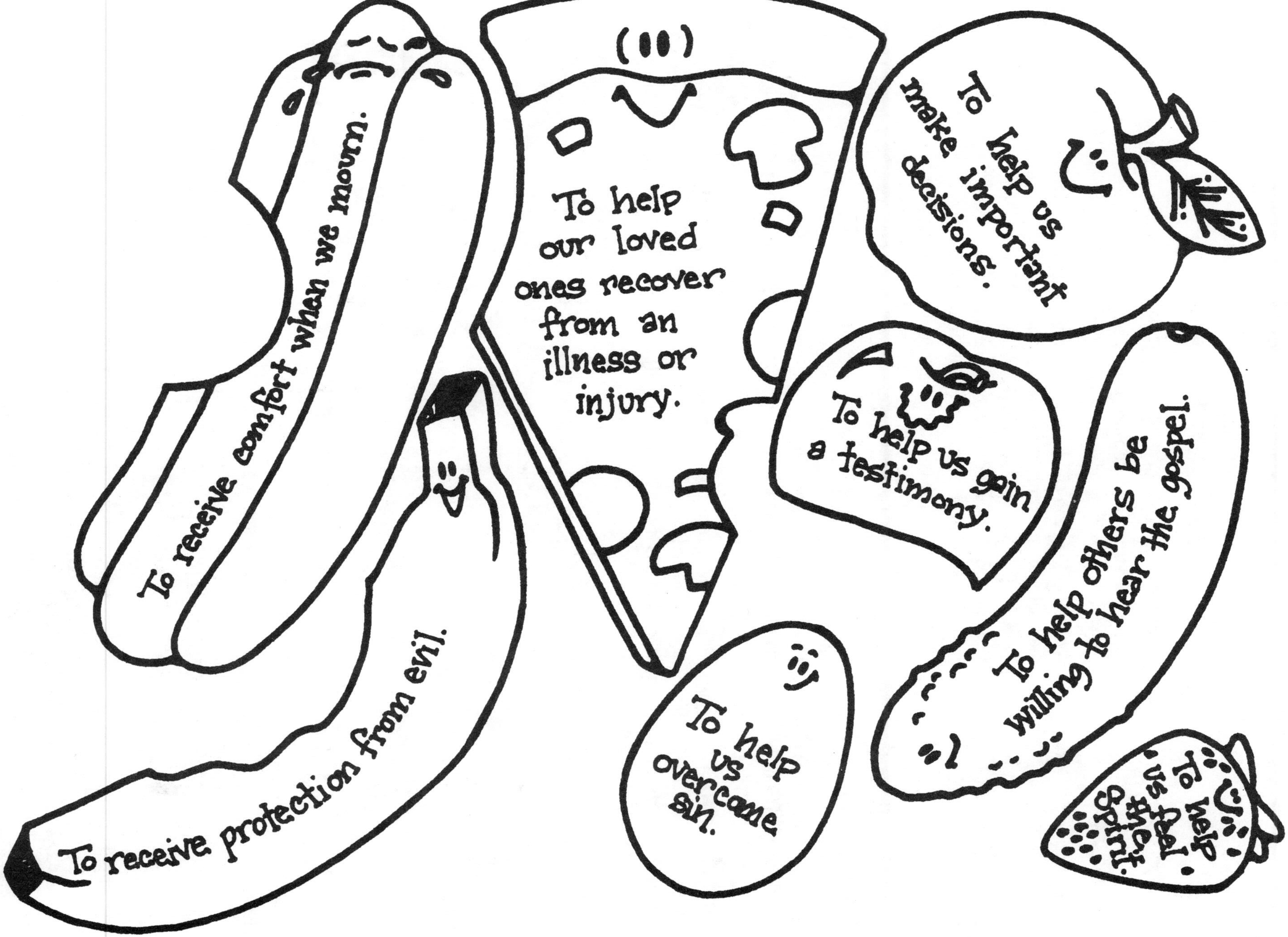
To receive comfort when we mourn.
To receive protection from evil.
To help our loved ones recover from an illness or injury.
To help us make important decisions.
To help us gain a testimony.
To help others be willing to hear the gospel.
To help us overcome sin.
To help us feel the Spirit.

*Lesson #39** — FAITH Helps Me to Be Strong and Overcome Trials

(Trials to Make Me Strong bird pop-up)

Trials make me strong so I can return to my Heavenly Father. Trials are necessary to make me strong, just as the tiny bird must work his way out of his shell. Trials give me strength!
D&C 136:31

YOU'LL NEED: Copy of Scripture Challenge card (page 112), Trials to Make Me Strong bird pop-up (page 77), on colored cardstock paper, and a straw for each child, scissors, glue, tape, and crayons or markers.

Review Enrichment Activity #1 (page 173) in Primary 6 Old Testament manual.*

ACTIVITY: Help children think about trials that make them strong spiritually as you read Job 27:2-5, D&C 121:7-10, and D&C 136:31. Tell children that faith in Heavenly Father and Jesus Christ will help them overcome trials. We can increase our faith to become strong to overcome trials as we read the scriptures and obey the commandments. Each time we overcome a trial we become stronger for the next trial. To make bird head pop up, follow these steps. (1) Color and cut out eggs and bird head. (2) Tape straw to inside of one bird head. (3) Glue bird heads together. (4) Lay straw and bird head on the inside of egg. (5) Glue blank sides of eggs together leaving the top and bottom open for the straw with the bird head. (6) Move straw and bird head up and down in pecking motion as you read the message.

SCRIPTURE CHALLENGE: Do activity in class or at home.

THOUGHT TREAT: Trial Trail Mix. Mix cereal, nuts, chocolate or carob chips, raisins, and other dried fruit to make a trail mix. Place some in individual bags. As you munch, tell children, "This is trial trail mix. As you look at the different ingredients in this trail mix, think of the different trials you might face as you follow the straight and narrow trail back to our Heavenly Father."

*Lesson #40** — WORD OF WISDOM: I Will Keep This Law of Health

(Word of Wisdom Choices match puzzle)

YOU'LL NEED: Copy of Scripture Challenge card (page 112) and Word of Wisdom Choices match puzzle (page 78) on colored paper for each child, pencils, tape, and crayons.

ACTIVITY: Help children think of the Word of Wisdom choices. Learn which choices make us happy and healthy and which choices make us sad and unhealthy.

Review Enrichment Activity #1 (page 177) in Primary 6 Old Testament manual.*

PUZZLE MATCH: Read instructions on puzzle to match up pictures and draw smile and frown faces. Draw a straight face on D&C 89:12 (as it tells us that meat should be eaten "*sparingly*.").

TEACHING TOOL: Place pictures next to scriptures so the scriptures show or tape them over the scriptures at the top to create a flap. Encourage children to share this with their family.

SCRIPTURE CHALLENGE: Do in class or at home.

THOUGHT TREAT: Healthy Snacks. Share with children a slice of whole grain bread, fruit or vegetable, or other healthy snack.

**Primary 6* manual is published by The Church of Jesus Christ of Latter-day Saints, Salt Lake City, Utah.

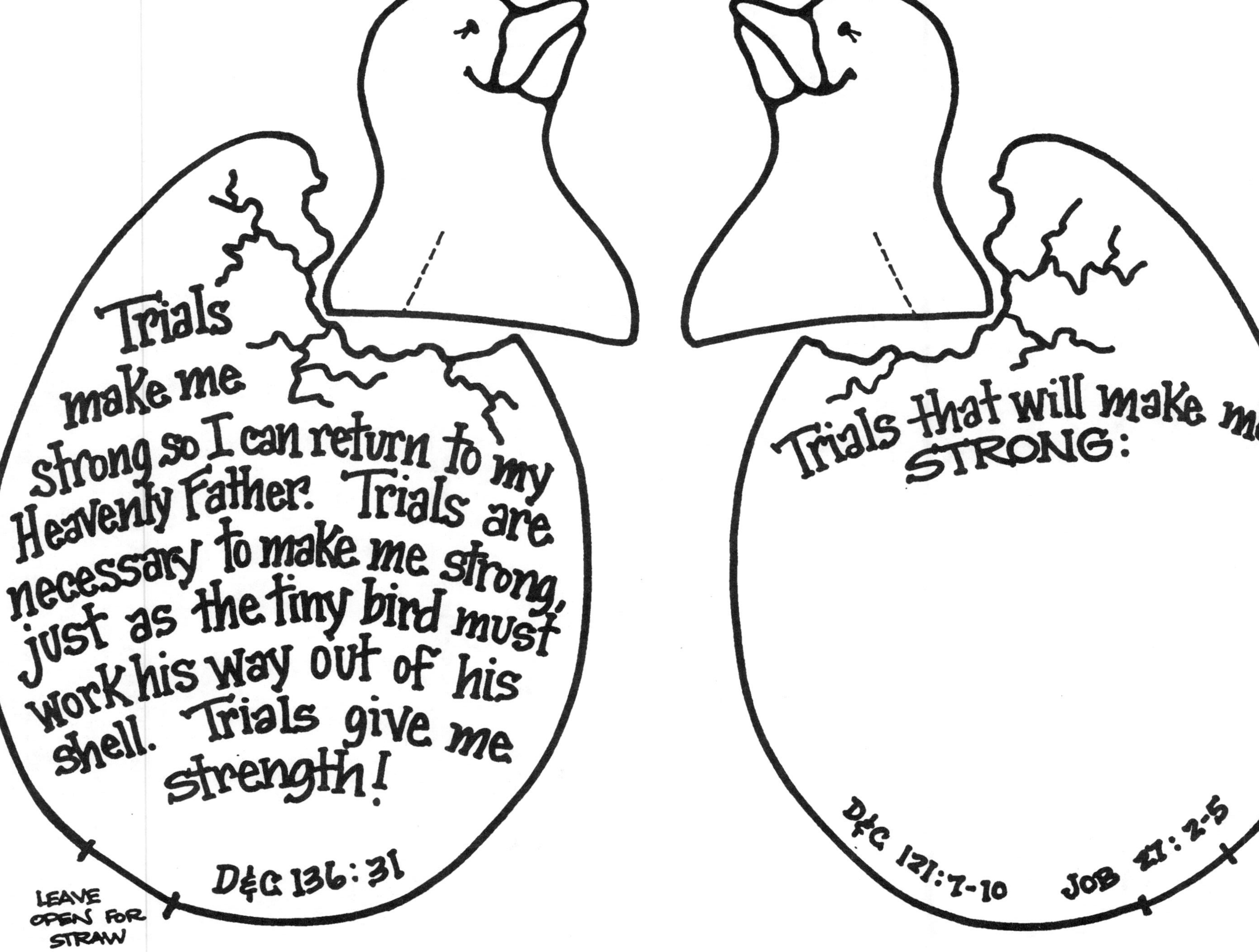

Trials
make me
strong so I can return to my
Heavenly Father. Trials are
necessary to make me strong,
just as the tiny bird must
work his way out of his
shell. Trials give me
strength!
D&C 136:31
LEAVE OPEN FOR STRAW
Trials that will make me
STRONG:
D&C 121:7-10
JOB 27:2-5

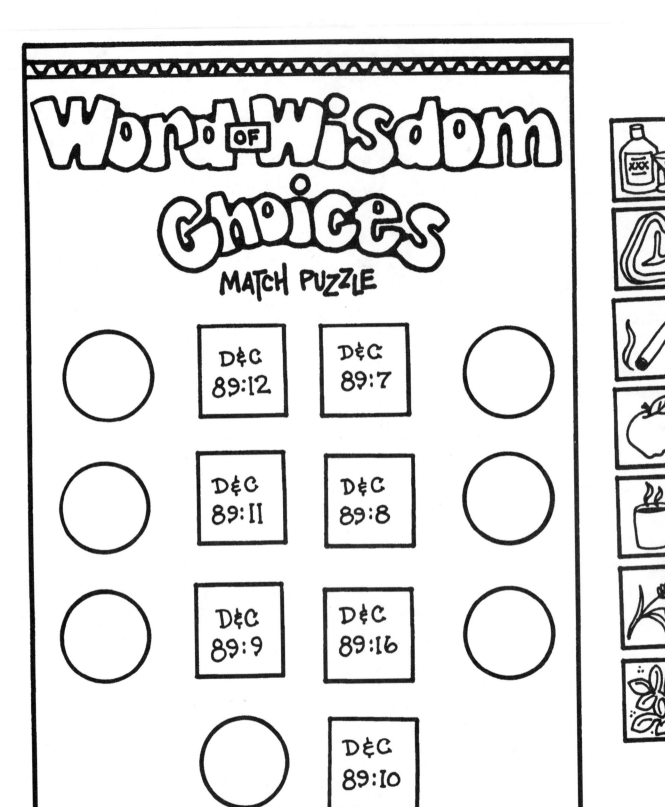

Word of Wisdom Choices

MATCH PUZZLE

D&C 89:12	D&C 89:7
D&C 89:11	D&C 89:8
D&C 89:9	D&C 89:16
	D&C 89:10

Read each scripture and paste the corresponding sticker in the square. Then draw a smile face for those things that are good for you and a frowny face for things that are not good for you.

Lesson #41* **TESTIMONY: The Gospel of Jesus Christ Is True**
(Valiant Testimony board game)

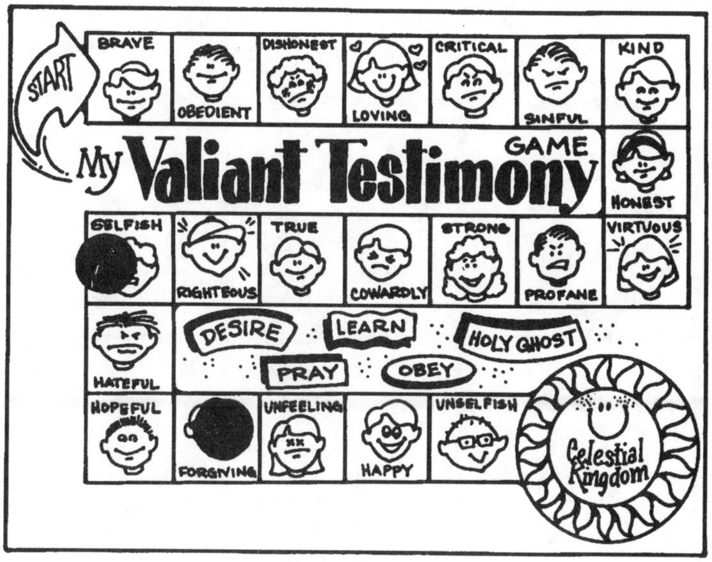

YOU'LL NEED: Copy of Scripture Challenge card (page 113) and Valiant Testimony board game, testimony cards #1-42 and game rules (pages 80-82) on colored cardstock paper for each child, two coin or button markers, twenty or more wordstrips with "1," "2," or "3" written on each, a container for wordstrips, scissors, and crayons or markers.

ACTIVITY: Help children learn ways they can strengthen their testimonies of Jesus Christ and his gospel. Color and cut out board game and testimony cards. See game rules and answers on page 81.

Review Enrichment Activity #4 (page 183) in Primary 6 Old Testament manual.*

SCRIPTURE CHALLENGE: Do activity in class or at home.

THOUGHT TREAT: "Bee" Valiant Honey Taffy. Bring to a medium boil 1 cup of honey, boiling 7-10 minutes. Cook to a soft ball stage (test by dropping 1/4 teaspoon into cold water). Cool three minutes and pull into taffy, adding butter as you pull. Cut into bite-size pieces to share. Talk to children about "bee"ing valiant, obeying Heavenly Father's commandments. Talk about what they can look forward to if they are obedient, e.g., having safety and peace in this life and later living with Heavenly Father and Jesus in the celestial kingdom.

Lesson #42* **PRAYER: I Will Pray Morning and Night**
(I Love to Pray prayer suggestions spiral)

YOU'LL NEED: Copy of Scripture Challenge card (page 113) and I Love to Pray spiral (page 83) on colored cardstock paper for each child, pencils, and light/bright watercolor markers.

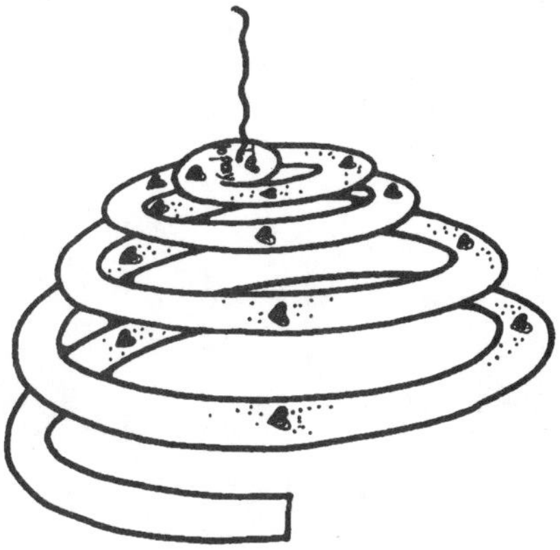

ACTIVITY: Help children write on the spiral things they are thankful for and things they might pray for morning and night. Color and cut out spiral. Tie a knot in an 8" piece of ribbon to hang above their bed as a reminder.

Review Enrichment Activities #2 and #4 (page 187) in Primary 6 Old Testament manual.*

SCRIPTURE CHALLENGE: Do in class or at home.

THOUGHT TREAT: Prayer Popcorn. Tell children, "Just as popcorn pops with the effort of heat, our faith can 'pop' into our lives as we make the effort to kneel down and talk to our Heavenly Father."

*Primary 6 manual is published by The Church of Jesus Christ of Latter-day Saints, Salt Lake City, Utah.

START
My Valiant Testimony GAME
BRAVE
OBEDIENT
DISHONEST
LOVING
CRITICAL
SINFUL
KIND
HONEST
VIRTUOUS
PROFANE
STRONG
COWARDLY
TRUE
RIGHTEOUS
SELFISH
HATEFUL
DESIRE
LEARN
PRAY
OBEY
HOLY GHOST
HOPEFUL
FORGIVING
UNFEELING
HAPPY
UNSELFISH
Celestial Kingdom

PATTERN: *TESTIMONY (Valiant Testimony board game cards)*

How to Play "MY VALIANT TESTIMONY" Game:

1. Divide into two teams.
2. Mix up testimony cards #1-42 and place face down.
3. Use a coin or button marker for each team and place on START.
4. Take turns drawing number (1, 2, or 3) wordstrips out of a container and move that number of spaces on the board.
5. If you land on an non-valiant action word (with frowny face), move back one space.
6. If you land on a valiant action word (with smile face), draw a testimony card.
7. Read the testimony card and guess the missing key word (found on the game board): DESIRE, PRAY, LEARN, OBEY, or HOLY GHOST.
8. Place card in a pile until all wordstrips are read, then place wordstrips back in container to play again.
9. Score 10 points for guessing the key word right. See answers listed below.
10. The first team to reach Celestial Kingdom wins, or the first team to earn 100 points.

ANSWERS: DESIRE (Cards #1, 2, 22, 31, 40, 41, 42)
PRAY (Cards #3, 4, 14, 15, 23, 24, 32)
LEARN (Cards #5, 6, 7, 8, 16, 17, 25, 26, 33, 34, 39)
OBEY (Cards #9, 10, 18, 19, 27, 30, 35, 36)
HOLY GHOST (Cards #11, 12, 13, 20, 21, 28, 29, 37, 38)

MOVE 1	MOVE 2	MOVE 3	MOVE 1	MOVE 2	MOVE 3	MOVE 1	MOVE 2	MOVE 3
MOVE 1	MOVE 2	MOVE 3	MOVE 1	MOVE 2	MOVE 3	MOVE 1	MOVE 2	MOVE 3
MOVE 1	MOVE 2	MOVE 3	MOVE 1	MOVE 2	MOVE 3	MOVE 1	MOVE 2	MOVE 3
MOVE 1	MOVE 2	MOVE 3	MOVE 1	MOVE 2	MOVE 3	MOVE 1	MOVE 2	MOVE 3

TESTIMONY CARD #1:

We __________ to gain a stronger testimony of the gospel of Jesus Christ.

TESTIMONY CARD #2:

This __________ helps us want to work to receive a testimony.

TESTIMONY CARD #3:

We _________ to Heavenly Father and tell him of our desire to know that Jesus Christ is our Savior

TESTIMONY CARD #4:

We can __________ to know that the gospel is true.

TESTIMONY CARD #5:

We ___________ about Jesus and what he wants us to do.

TESTIMONY CARD #6:

As we read the scriptures we ___________ about Jesus.

TESTIMONY CARD #7:

We ___________ about Jesus by attending family home evening, Primary, and sacrament meeting.

TESTIMONY CARD #8:

We __________ about Jesus by listening to our parents, teachers, the living prophet, and other righteous leaders.

TESTIMONY CARD #9:

If we want to know the gospel of Jesus Christ is true, we _______ (which means to live it).

TESTIMONY CARD #10:

We _______ the commandments and follow the teachings of Jesus.

TESTIMONY CARD #11:

Our testimonies come to us through the ________ ________.

TESTIMONY CARD #12:

The ________ ________ speaks to our hearts and minds.

TESTIMONY CARD #13:

The _________ __________ lets us know within ourselves that the gospel is true.

TESTIMONY CARD #14:

We ___________ in the name of Jesus Christ.

TESTIMONY CARD #15:

I will search, ponder, and ___________ about the scriptures each day.

TESTIMONY CARD #16:

When you go to school, listen and ___________ to get a good education.

TESTIMONY CARD #17:

As we ___________ of Nephi's courage, we find it easy to choose the right.

TESTIMONY CARD #18:

I do what my parents say. This way I am learning to _________.

TESTIMONY CARD #19:

I will do what the prophets say. This means I will ___________.

TESTIMONY CARD #20:

I am not alone. Jesus sent the ___________ __________ to comfort me.

TESTIMONY CARD #21:

The _________ __________ tells me what I need to change.

TESTIMONY CARD #22:

The __________ to be healthy makes us want to live the Word of Wisdom.

TESTIMONY CARD #23:

____________ to be an example to others. Each day, show them how to live the righteous way.

TESTIMONY CARD #24:

James 1:5 tells us to __________ to "ask of God"" if something is true.

TESTIMONY CARD #25:

When a family ___________s together, a family stays together.

TESTIMONY CARD #26:

What you ___________ in this life is a heavenly treasure, something you can take with you when you die.

TESTIMONY CARD #27:

The more we __________ about the gospel of Jesus Christ, the happier we feel.

TESTIMONY CARD #28:

When I partake of the sacrament on the Sabbath day, I promise to ____________.

TESTIMONY CARD #29:

The _________ _________ is my guide. He is my spirit's guide.

TESTIMONY CARD #30:

The happy feeling in my heart, lets me know the ___________ ___________ is there for me.

TESTIMONY CARD #31:

Each time I pray, I learn new ways to ___________.

TESTIMONY CARD #32:

The ___________ to show gratitude helps us say, "Thank you."

TESTIMONY CARD #33:

Reading the scriptures helps us ___________ to be happy.

TESTIMONY CARD #34:

I kneel to ___________ every day to thank Heavenly Father and say what is in my heart.

TESTIMONY CARD #35:

We ____________ about our ancestors when we do our family history.

TESTIMONY CARD #36:

As we _____________ to make good choices, we can stay on heaven's straight and narrow path.

TESTIMONY CARD #37:

I will _________, which means to choose the righteous way.

TESTIMONY CARD #38:

When I say OK, this means I will _________.

TESTIMONY CARD #39:

The still small voice of the ___________ __________ teaches me to know the truth.

TESTIMONY CARD #40:

The _________ _________ is my true, eternal friend.

TESTIMONY CARD #41:

___________ to be kind, to love others as Jesus did.

TESTIMONY CARD #42:

Because we _________ to share the gospel, we bear our testimony.

PATTERN: *PRAYER (I Love to Pray prayer suggestions spiral)*

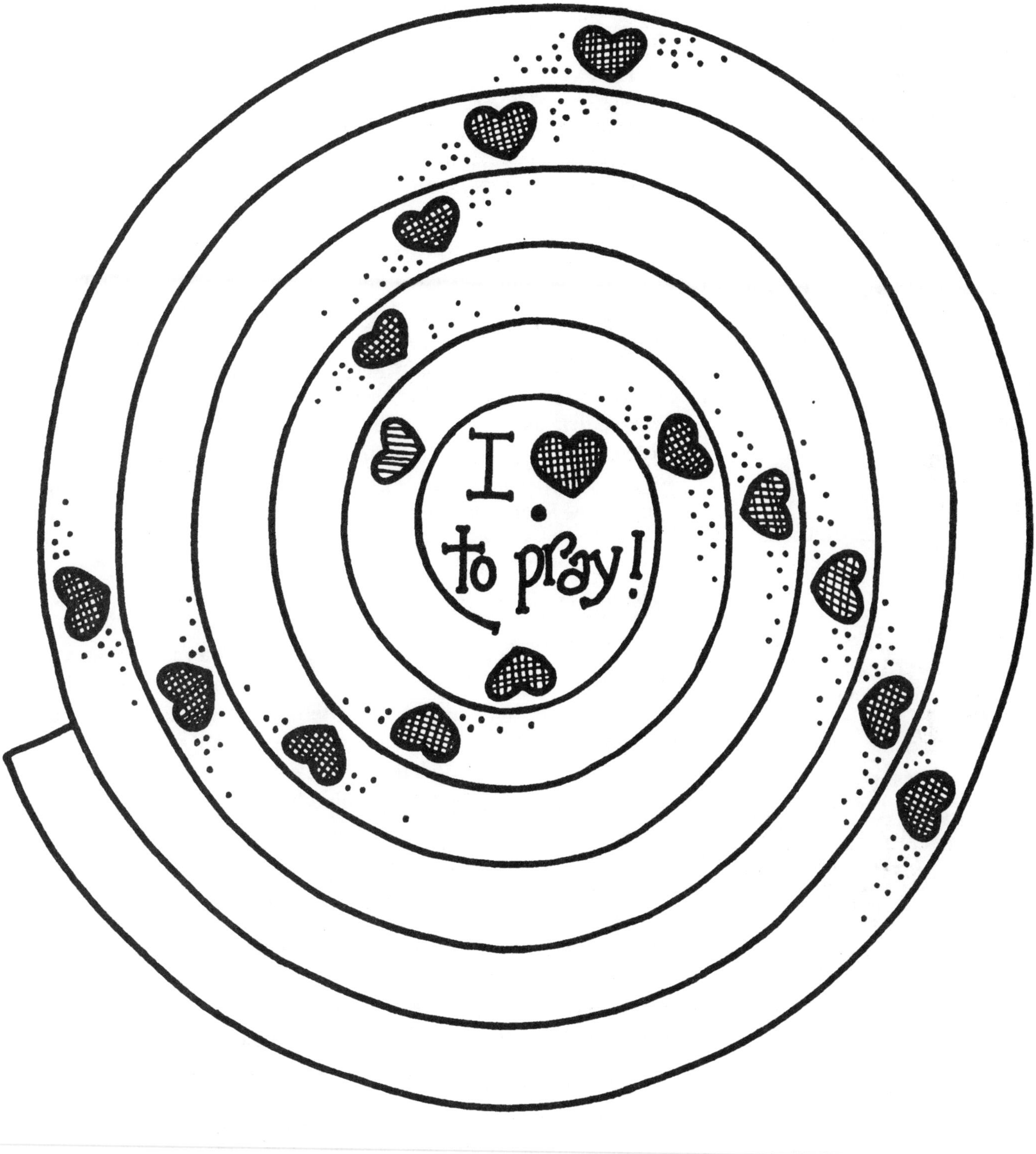

*Lesson #43**

REPENTANCE: Heavenly Father Forgives All Who Truly Repent

(Bite-size Memorize repentance challenge)

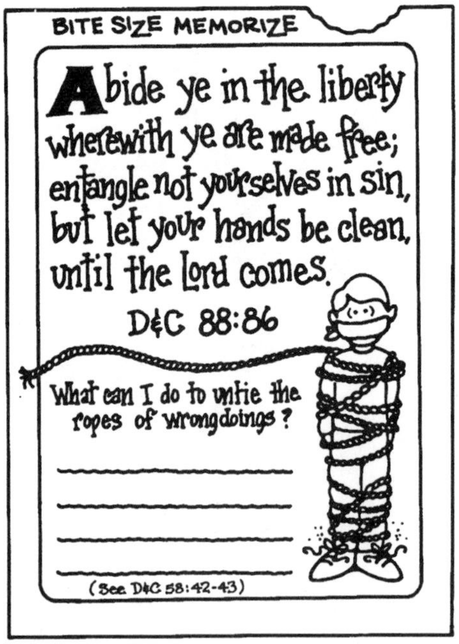
BITE SIZE MEMORIZE
Abide ye in the liberty wherewith ye are made free; entangle not yourselves in sin, but let your hands be clean, until the Lord comes.
D&C 88:86
What can I do to untie the ropes of wrongdoings?
(See D&C 58:42-43)

YOU'LL NEED: Copy of Scripture Challenge card (page 114), and bite-size memorize (page 85) on colored cardstock paper for each child, pencils, and crayons.

ACTIVITIES: (1) Compare wrongdoings to the rope that entangles us. Help children memorize D&C 88:86. Let children know that our free agency is important to feel happy. When we are entangled in sin, we feel unhappy.

Review Enrichment Activities #1 and #5 (pages 191-192) in Primary 6 Old Testament manual.*

(2) Help children list three things they can do to untie the ropes of wrongdoings found in D&C 58:42-43: have sorrow—repenting of sin, confessing sins, and forsaking sins.

SCRIPTURE CHALLENGE: Do activity in class or at home.

THOUGHT TREAT: Repentance Rope Licorice. Purchase Pull-and-Peel licorice (6 strands of licorice in a rope to pull apart). Tell children that sin can entangle us. Pull licorice strands apart and say, "Repentance sets us free from the binding influence of Satan. When we say 'no' to temptation we cannot be bound by the effects of sin. We are free to choose the right."

*Lesson #44**

TITHING: I Will Pay Honest Tithes and Offerings

(pending spending envelope)

Pending Spending
I must wait to spend my cash until my tithing's paid; It makes "cents" for me to give and show I have obeyed.

YOU'LL NEED: Copy of Scripture Challenge card (page 114), and pending spending envelope (page 86) on colored cardstock paper for each child, scissors, glue, tithing and offering receipts, and crayons or markers. OPTION: Color and laminate envelope ahead of time, glue Velcro or use sticky-back Velcro to close envelope.

ACTIVITY: Create a pending spending envelope where children can store their income until they can divide it into tithes and offerings, savings, and spending. This will help them avoid the temptation to spend tithing. Once it's divided they can place their donations in the tithing and offerings envelope.

Review Enrichment Activity #3 (page 199) in Primary 6 Old Testament manual.*

SCRIPTURE CHALLENGE: Do activity in class or at home.

THOUGHT TREAT: Tithing Toast. Cut a piece of toast in half with crust removed to create bills. Cut round coin shapes with a bottle lid. Place toast bill and 10 toast coins in a clear zip-close bag.

TO MAKE TOAST: Butter bread and sprinkle colored sugar (green for bills and yellow for coins. To mix sugar, add food coloring to granulated sugar and mix in a plastic zip-close bag). Broil buttered and sugared toast 2-3 minutes in the oven. Tell children that they can become "toast" in the latter-days when the earth is cleansed by fire if they do not pay their tithing. Read the following scriptures: D&C 64:23 and D&C 85:3.

D&C 64:23 *"He that is tithed shall not be burned at his coming."*

D&C 85:3 *"He may tithe his people, to prepare them against the day of vengeance and burning."*

*Primary 6 manual is published by The Church of Jesus Christ of Latter-day Saints, Salt Lake City, Utah.

BITE SIZE MEMORIZE

Abide ye in the liberty wherewith ye are made free; entangle not yourselves in sin, but let your hands be clean, until the Lord comes.

D&C 88:86

What can I do to untie the ropes of wrongdoings?

____

____

____

____

(See D&C 58:42-43)

PATTERN: *TITHING (pending spending envelope)*

Pending
Spending
I must wait to spend my cash
until my tithing's paid.
It makes "cents" for me to give
and show I have obeyed.

*Lesson #45** **ATONEMENT: Jesus Gave Me Immortality and Eternal Life**
(Atonement object lesson)

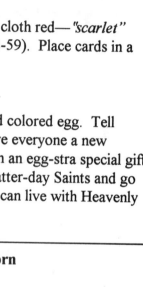

YOU'LL NEED: Copy of Scripture Challenge card (page 115) and Atonement object cards (page 88) on colored cardstock paper, and a plastic bag or envelope for each child, scissors, pencils, and crayons.

Review Enrichment Activity #6 (page 205-206) in Primary 6 Old Testament manual.*

ACTIVITY: Place real objects with Atonement object cards attached or just the object cards in a basket or sack. Ask children to take turns drawing an object card. Ask them to tell the meaning of the scripture and how it relates to the object. Ask children to take their cards home, read the scripture, and write the meaning in the blank lines below. Example: on the coins card—Matthew 26:14-16 they could write: "Jesus was betrayed for 30 pieces of silver." Ask children to color one cloth red—*"scarlet"* (Matthew 27:28-30) and leave the other cloth white—*"clean linen"* (Matthew 27:58-59). Place cards in a bag or envelope to keep.

SCRIPTURE CHALLENGE CARD: Do activity in class or assign to do at home.

THOUGHT TREAT: Eternal Life Egg-stra Special Treat. Give each child a boiled colored egg. Tell children the egg represents a new beginning. Jesus Christ gave his life for us and gave everyone a new beginning, immortality (to be resurrected). Jesus also gave everyone a chance to earn an egg-stra special gift, the gift of eternal life. Those who are baptized into The Church of Jesus Christ of Latter-day Saints and go the "egg-stra mile" by living the commandments and receiving the temple ordinances can live with Heavenly Father and Jesus again in the celestial kingdom.

*Lesson #46** **CHRISTMAS: Jesus, Heavenly Father's Son, Is Born**
(testimony star and star ornament)

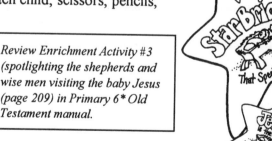

YOU'LL NEED: Copy of Scripture Challenge card (page 115) and large and small stars (page 89) on colored cardstock paper for each child, scissors, pencils, yarn, paper punch, and crayons.

Review Enrichment Activity #3 (spotlighting the shepherds and wise men visiting the baby Jesus (page 209) in Primary 6 Old Testament manual.*

ACTIVITY: Help children share their testimony of Jesus Christ and create an ornament to remember Him. Color and cut out a star for each child.

TESTIMONY STAR: Ask each child to write their testimony or write key words that describe their testimony on the back of the large star. Take turns sharing your testimony and how you feel about the Savior. Ask children to take the large star home and place it in their window, sharing their testimony with their family.

STAR ORNAMENT: Punch a hole in the small star and attach a 6" piece of yarn to create an ornament child can hand on their Christmas tree.

SCRIPTURE CHALLENGE CARD: Do activity in class or assign to do at home.

THOUGHT TREAT: Star-Shaped Cookies.

**Primary 6* manual is published by The Church of Jesus Christ of Latter-day Saints, Salt Lake City, Utah.

Objects that relate to the

ATONEMENT

of Jesus Christ

Matthew 27: 50-51

Matthew 26: 14-16

Matthew 27: 60-65

Matthew 27: 24-26

Matthew 27:58-59

Matthew 27: 31-32

Matthew 27: 28-30

Star Bright
That Special Night!
Jesus
is the star
we've waited for!

*Lesson #47**

PRIESTHOOD: I Will Live Worthily to Receive Priesthood Blessings

(My Gospel Standards sentence search)

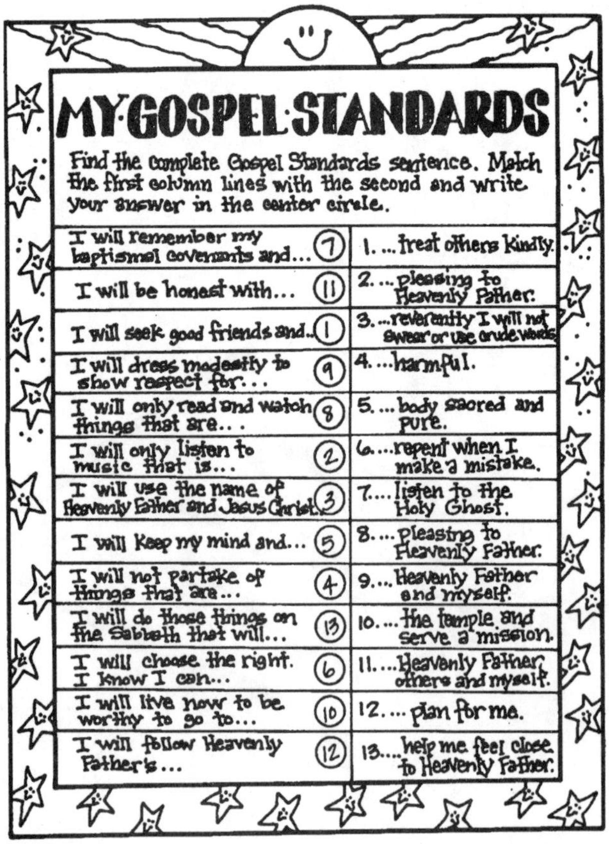

YOU'LL NEED: Copy of Scripture Challenge card (page 116) and My Gospel Standards sentence search (page 91) on colored cardstock paper for each child, Achievement Days booklet* with Gospel Standards on back (optional), pencils, and markers.

ACTIVITY: Help children learn the gospel standards they are asked to follow by completing the following sentence search.

Review Enrichment Activity #1 and #4 (page 214-216) in Primary 6 Old Testament manual.*

MY GOSPEL STANDARDS SENTENCE SEARCH:

To find the complete Gospel Standard sentence; match the first column lines with the second column lines by writing the number in the center circle. Example: The partial statement "***I will remember my baptismal covenants and***" matches with #7 "***listen to the Holy Ghost.***" Place the number "7" in the center circle.

ANSWERS (Numbers to place in circles):
7, 11, 1, 9, 2 or 8, 2 or 8, 3, 5, 4, 13, 6, 10, 12

Let children know that as they follow these gospel standards, they will be worthy to receive priesthood blessings. Review lesson 33 (page 147) in *Primary* 6 manual*.

PRIESTHOOD BLESSINGS WE CAN RECEIVE BY LIVING THE GOSPEL STANDARDS:

♥ Blessing babies ♥ Baptism ♥ Laying on of hands for the gift of the Holy Ghost
♥ Sacrament ♥ Administration to the sick ♥ Father's blessings
♥ Ordination to the priesthood ♥ Temple ordinances
♥ Being set apart for missions or callings

SCRIPTURE CHALLENGE CARD: Do activity in class or assign to do at home.

THOUGHT TREAT: Peanut Butter Priesthood Pizza Cookie. Make a batch of peanut butter cookie dough, spread it on a greased round pizza pan. Bake 350° oven 13-15 minutes or until golden brown. NOTE: As pizza cookie is cooling place 9 chocolate Hershey's Kisses® (unwrapped) on top. Tell children that the 9 pieces represent the 9 priesthood blessings noted above. Slice a piece of pizza cookie for each child with a chocolate kiss on top. Cut cookie with a pizza cutter in a triangle pizza shape.
If there are more than 9 children in class, cut pizza slices in half to serve 18 children.

PEANUT BUTTER PIZZA COOKIE DOUGH: 1/2 cup butter or margarine, 1/2 cup peanut butter, 3/4 cup brown sugar, 1/4 cup granulated sugar, 1 egg, 1 teaspoon vanilla, 1/4 teaspoon salt, 1 3/4 cups flour, 1/2 teaspoon baking soda, 1/2 teaspoon baking powder, 4 tablespoons granulated sugar.

Primary 6 manual is published by The Church of Jesus Christ of Latter-day Saints, Salt Lake City, Utah.

MY·GOSPEL·STANDARDS

Find the complete Gospel Standards sentence. Match the first column lines with the second and write your answer in the center circle.

I will remember my baptismal covenants and...	○	1. ...treat others kindly.
I will be honest with...	○	2. ...pleasing to Heavenly Father
I will seek good friends and...	○	3. ...reverently. I will not swear or use crude words.
I will dress modestly to show respect for...	○	4. ...harmful.
I will only read and watch things that are...	○	5. ...body sacred and pure.
I will only listen to music that is...	○	6. ...repent when I make a mistake.
I will use the name of Heavenly Father and Jesus Christ...	○	7. ...listen to the Holy Ghost.
I will keep my mind and...	○	8. ...pleasing to Heavenly Father.
I will not partake of things that are...	○	9. ...Heavenly Father and myself.
I will do those things on the Sabbath that will...	○	10. ...the temple and serve a mission.
I will choose the right. I know I can...	○	11. ...Heavenly Father, others and myself.
I will live now to be worthy to go to...	○	12. ...plan for me.
I will follow Heavenly Father's...	○	13. ...help me feel close to Heavenly Father.

Front and back cover for Scripture Challenge cards #1-47 to match lesson #1-47 in Primary 6 Old Testament manual.*

☺

☺

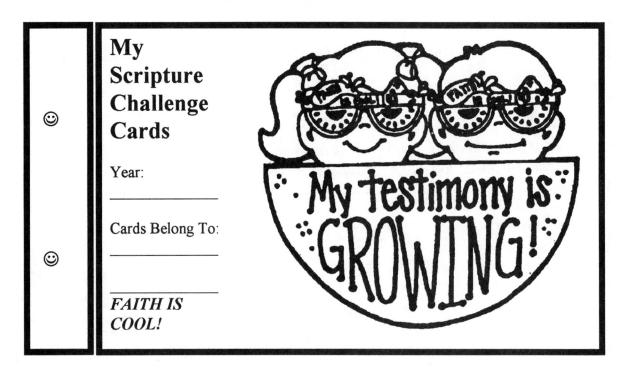

My Scripture Challenge Cards

Year:

____

Cards Belong To:

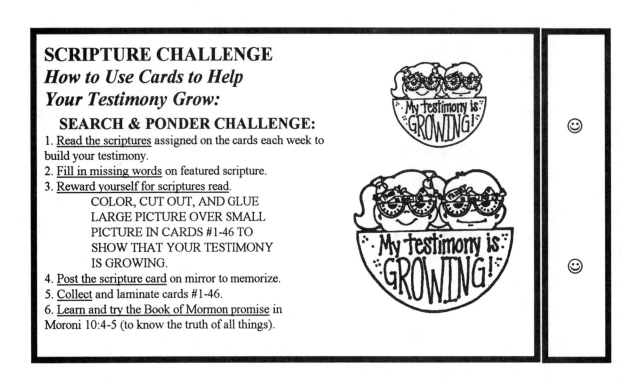

____

____

FAITH IS COOL!

SCRIPTURE CHALLENGE

How to Use Cards to Help Your Testimony Grow:

SEARCH & PONDER CHALLENGE:

1. Read the scriptures assigned on the cards each week to build your testimony.
2. Fill in missing words on featured scripture.
3. Reward yourself for scriptures read.
   COLOR, CUT OUT, AND GLUE LARGE PICTURE OVER SMALL PICTURE IN CARDS #1-46 TO SHOW THAT YOUR TESTIMONY IS GROWING.
4. Post the scripture card on mirror to memorize.
5. Collect and laminate cards #1-46.
6. Learn and try the Book of Mormon promise in Moroni 10:4-5 (to know the truth of all things).

☺

☺

*Primary 6 manual is published by The Church of Jesus Christ of Latter-day Saints, Salt Lake City, Utah.

HEAVENLY FATHER'S PLAN #1

Plan Is for Me

SEARCH & PONDER CHALLENGE:
Read: Job 38:4, 7 and Abraham 3:22-26

Abraham 3:25-26 "And we will __ __ __ __ __ them herewith, to see if they will do all things whatsoever the Lord their God shall command them; And they who keep their first estate shall be added upon; and they who keep not their first estate shall not have __ __ __ __ __ in the same kingdom with those who keep their first estate; and they who keep their second estate shall have glory added upon their heads for ever and __ __ __ __."

JESUS CHRIST #2

Was Chosen to Be My Savior

SEARCH & PONDER CHALLENGE:
Read: Moses 4:1-4

Moses 4:3-4 "Wherefore, because that Satan __ __ __ __ __ __ __ __ __ __ against me, and sought to destroy the __ __ __ __ __ __ __ of man, which I, the Lord God, had given him, and also, that I should give unto him mine own power; by the power of mine Only Begotten, I caused that he should be cast down; And he became Satan, yea, even the devil, the father of all __ __ __ __, to deceive and to blind men, and to lead them captive at his will, even as many as would not hearken unto my voice."

CREATION: #3

Heavenly Father and Jesus Created the Earth for Me

SEARCH & PONDER CHALLENGE:
Read: Genesis 1:26-31

Genesis 1:26, 31 "And God said, Let us make man in our image, after our likeness: and let them have dominion over the __ __ __ __ of the sea, and over the __ __ __ __ of the air, and over the __ __ __ __ __ __ __, and over all the earth, and over every __ __ __ __ __ __ __ __ __ thing that creepeth upon the earth. . . . And God saw every thing that he had made, and, behold, it was very good."

ETERNAL LIFE: #4

I Will Return to My Heavenly Home

SEARCH & PONDER CHALLENGE:
Read: Moses 5:9-12

Moses 5:10-11 Adam said, "Blessed be the name of God, for because of my transgression my eyes are __ __ __ __ __ __ __, and in this life I shall have joy, and again in the flesh I shall see God." Eve said, "Were it not for our transgression we never should have had seed, and never should have known good and evil, and the joy of our redemption, and the __ __ __ __ __ __ __ life which God giveth unto all the __ __ __ __ __ __ __ __ __ __ __."

☺

SACRIFICE:

#5

I Will Always Remember Jesus

SEARCH & PONDER CHALLENGE:
Read: Moses 5:4-8

Moses 5:8

"Thou shalt _ _ all that thou doest in the

_ _ _ _ of the _ _ _, and thou shalt

_ _ _ _ _ _ _ and call upon God in the

☺ name of the Son

_ _ _ _ _ _ _ _ _ _ _ _ _ _ _."

☺

ETERNAL LIFE

#6

I Will Live the Gospel of Jesus Christ

SEARCH & PONDER CHALLENGE:
Read: Moses 6:52, 64-68 and
2 Nephi 31:15-21

2 Nephi 31:20 "Ye must press forward with a
_ _ _ _ _ _ _ _ _ _ _ _ _ _ _ _ _ _ _ in
Christ, having a perfect brightness of hope, and a
_ _ _ _ _ of God and of all men. Wherefore, if ye
shall press forward, feasting upon the _ _ _ _ _
☺ of Christ, and _ _ _ _ _ _ _ _ to the end, behold,
thus saith the Father: Ye shall have
_ _ _ _ _ _ _ _ _ _ _ _ _ _."

☺

☺

ZION: #7

I Will Be Pure in Heart to Help Build Zion

SEARCH & PONDER CHALLENGE:
Read: Moses 7:18-21

Moses 7:18

"And the __ __ __ __ called his people __ __ __ __, because they were of one __ __ __ __ __ __ and one mind, and dwelt in righteousness; and there was no poor among them."

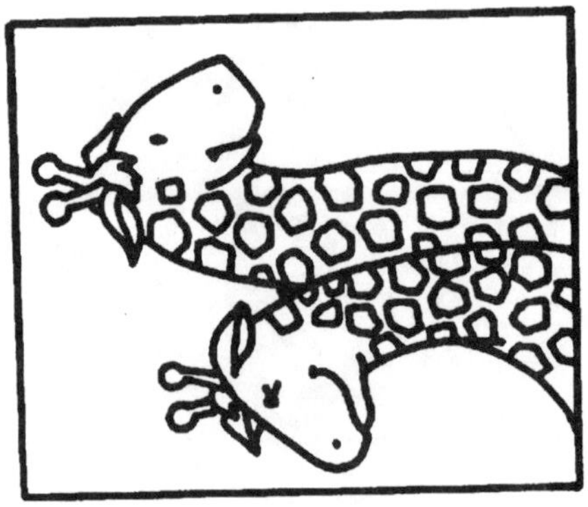

☺

☺

PROPHET: #8

I Will Listen to and Follow the Prophet

SEARCH & PONDER CHALLENGE:
Genesis 6:11-22; 7:1-6; 8:15-20

Genesis 6:19; 7:7, 9, 12 "And of every living thing of all flesh, __ __ __ of every sort shall thou bring into the ark, to keep them __ __ __ __ __ __ with thee; they shall be male and female . . . . And Noah went in, and his sons, and his wife, and his sons' wives with him, into the ark, because of the waters of the flood . . . . There went in two and two unto Noah into the ark . . . as God had commanded . . . . [It rained 40] days."

☺

☺

MISSION: #9

I Will Prepare for My Mission

SEARCH & PONDER CHALLENGE:
Read: Abraham 2:9-11

Abraham 2:10

"And I will _ _ _ _ _ _ them through thy

_ _ _ _ _; for as many as receive this

_ _ _ _ _ _ _ _ shall be called after thy

name, and shall be accounted thy

_ _ _ _ _, and shall rise up and bless thee, as

their _ _ _ _ _ _ _ _ _."

☺

☺

LOVE: #10

I Will Show Love to Others as I Serve

SEARCH & PONDER CHALLENGE:
Read: Genesis 13:1-11

Genesis 13:8 "And Abram said unto Lot, Let

there be no _ _ _ _ _ _ _ _, I pray thee,

between me and thee, and between my

_ _ _ _ _ _ _ _ _ and thy herdmen; for we

be _ _ _ _ _ _ _ _ _ _ _."

☺

☺

TRUST: #11

I Believe in Heavenly Father and Jesus Christ

SEARCH & PONDER CHALLENGE:
Read: Genesis 22:1-13

Genesis 22: 2, 8 God said, "Take now thy ___ ___ ___, thine only son Isaac, whom thou lovest, and get thee into the land of Moriah; and offer him there for a burnt offering upon one of the mountains which I will ___ ___ ___ ___ thee of . . . . And Abraham said, My son, God will ___ ___ ___ ___ ___ ___ ___ himself a lamb for a burnt offering."

☺

☺

TEMPLE MARRIAGE #12

Brings Eternal Blessings

SEARCH & PONDER CHALLENGE:
Read: Genesis 24:42-51, 58

The Lord guides Abraham's servant in choosing Rebekah as a wife for Isaac.

Genesis 24:43, 51 "I stand by the well of water; and it shall come to pass, that when the virgin cometh forth to draw water . . . I say . . . Give me . . . drink; . . . Behold, Rebekah is before thee, take her, and go, and let her be thy master's son's ___ ___ ___ ___."

☺

☺

CHOOSE THE RIGHT

#13

To Keep Heaven in Sight

SEARCH & PONDER CHALLENGE:
Read: Genesis 33:1-15

Proverbs 29:18 "He that keepeth the _ _ _, happy is he."
Mosiah 2:41 "Consider on the blessed and happy state of those that keep the commandments of _ _ _. For behold, they are blessed in all things, both temporal and spiritual, and if they hold out _ _ _ _ _ _ _ _ _ _ to the end they are received into heaven, that thereby they may dwell with God in a state of never- _ _ _ _ _ _ _ _ happiness."

☺

☺

HONESTY:

#14

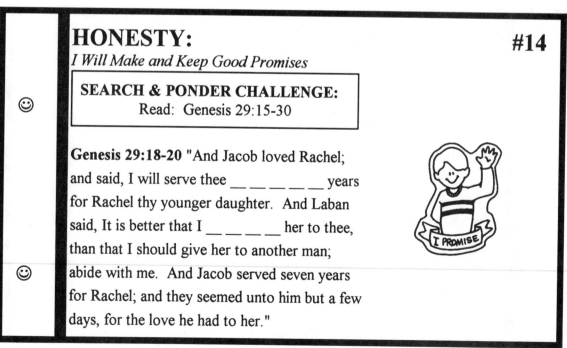

I Will Make and Keep Good Promises

SEARCH & PONDER CHALLENGE:
Read: Genesis 29:15-30

Genesis 29:18-20 "And Jacob loved Rachel; and said, I will serve thee _ _ _ _ _ _ years for Rachel thy younger daughter. And Laban said, It is better that I _ _ _ _ _ her to thee, than that I should give her to another man; abide with me. And Jacob served seven years for Rachel; and they seemed unto him but a few days, for the love he had to her."

☺

☺

ATTITUDE:

#15

My Faith in Jesus Christ Gives Me Courage

SEARCH & PONDER CHALLENGE:
Read: Genesis 37:18-36

Proverbs 17:22 "A merry _ _ _ _ _
doeth good like a medicine: but a broken
_ _ _ _ _ _ _ drieth the bones."

Romans 8:28 "And we know that all things
_ _ _ _ _ together for good to them that
_ _ _ _ _ God."

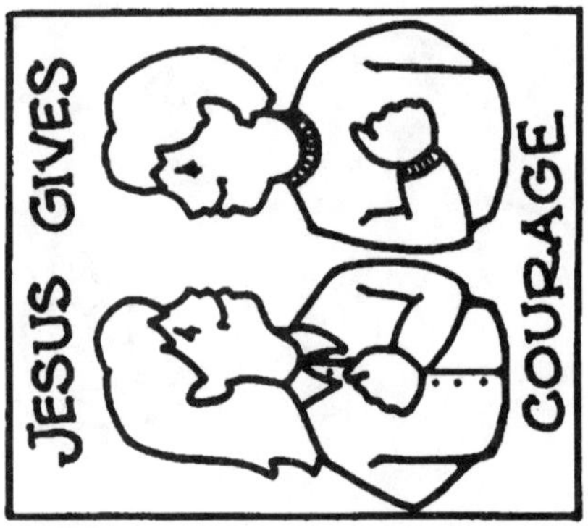

☺

☺

CHOOSE THE RIGHT:

#16

I Will Stay Away from Evil

SEARCH & PONDER CHALLENGE:
Read: Genesis 39

Psalm 24:3-5: "Who shall _ _ _ _ _ _ _
into the hill of the Lord? or who shall stand in
his holy place? He that hath _ _ _ _ _ _
hands, and a _ _ _ _ _ heart; who hath not
lifted up his soul unto _ _ _ _ _ _ _, nor
sworn deceitfully. He shall receive the
_ _ _ _ _ _ _ _ _ _ _ from the Lord, and
righteousness from the God of his salvation."

☺

☺

FORGIVENESS: #17

I Will Forgive Others

SEARCH & PONDER CHALLENGE:
Read: Genesis 45:1-8

Matthew 6:14-15 "If ye forgive men their

trespasses, your _ _ _ _ _ _ _ _ _ _

Father will also _ _ _ _ _ _ _ _ _ _ you:

But if ye forgive _ _ _ men their trespasses,

neither will your Father _ _ _ _ _ _ _ _ _ _

your trespasses."

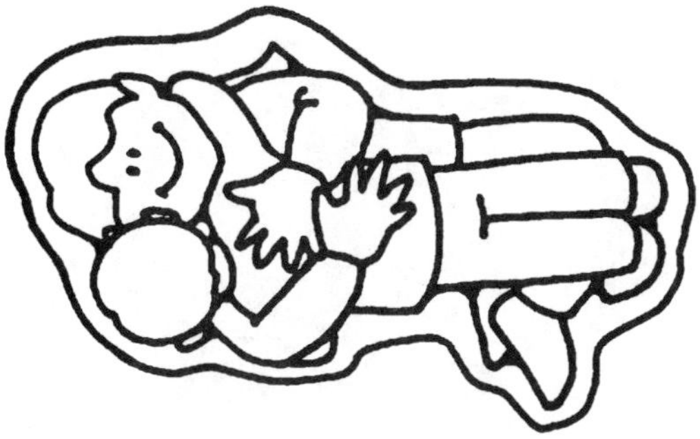

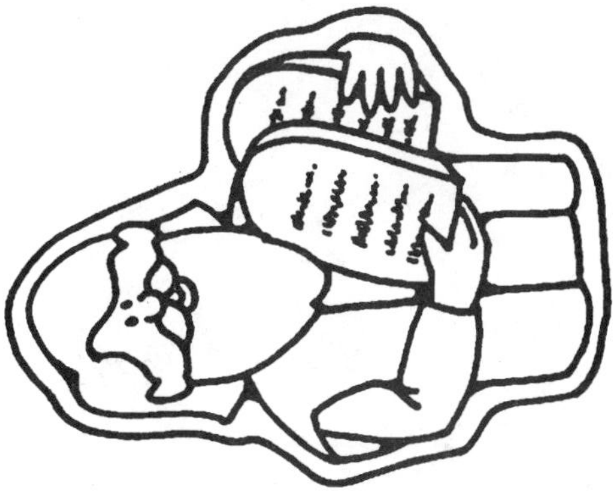

☺

☺

PREPARING #18

for My Life's Mission

SEARCH & PONDER CHALLENGE:
Read: Exodus 3:1-10

Moses 1:25-26 Blessed art thou,
_ _ _ _ _ _ _, for I, the Almighty, have
_ _ _ _ _ _ _ _ thee, and thou shalt be made
stronger than many _ _ _ _ _ _ _ _; for they
shall obey thy command as if thou wert God.
And lo, I am with thee, even unto the end of thy
days; for thou shalt _ _ _ _ _ _ _ _ _ _ my
people from bondage, even Israel my chosen."

PRIESTHOOD

#19

Is the Power of God

SEARCH & PONDER CHALLENGE:
Read: Exodus 14:21-31

Exodus 7:10 (the first miracle Moses and Aaron performed before Pharaoh)
"And Moses and Aaron went in unto Pharaoh, and they did so as the Lord had _ _ _ _ _ _ _ _ _ _ _: and Aaron cast down his rod before Pharaoh, and before his servants, and it became a _ _ _ _ _ _ _ _ _ _."

SABBATH DAY

#20

Is a Day of Worship and Joy

SEARCH & PONDER CHALLENGE:
Read: Exodus 16:2-8, 11-31

D&C 59:10, 13, 23 "This is a day appointed unto you to _ _ _ _ _ from your _ _ _ _ _ _ _ _ _, and to pay thy devotions unto the Most _ _ _ _ _ . . . . And on this day thou shalt do _ _ _ _ _ other thing . . . that thy _ _ _ _ may be made full . . . . He who doeth the works of righteousness shall receive his _ _ _ _ _ _ _ _ _, even peace in this world and eternal life in the world to come."

COMMANDMENTS

#21

Bring Light to My Life

SEARCH & PONDER CHALLENGE:
Read: Exodus 20:1-22

John 8:12 Jesus said, "I am the _ _ _ _ _ _ of the world: he that followeth me shall not _ _ _ _ _ in darkness, but shall have the light of life."

D&C 11:28 "Behold, I am Jesus Christ, the Son of God. I am the _ _ _ _ _ and the _ _ _ _ _ _ _ of the world."

Matthew 5:16 "Let your light so shine before men."

HUMILITY:

#22

I Am Willing to Be Taught by Others

SEARCH & PONDER CHALLENGE:
Numbers 21:6-9, John 3:14-15, D&C 112:10

Matthew 18:4 "Whosoever therefore shall humble himself as this little _ _ _ _ _ _ _, the same is the greatest in the kingdom of heaven."

D&C 1:37 "Search these commandments, for they are _ _ _ _ _ and faithful, and the prophecies and promises which are in them shall all be fulfilled."

D&C 112:10 "Be thou humble; and the Lord thy God shall lead thee by the hand, and give thee answers to thy _ _ _ _ _ _ _ _ _ _."

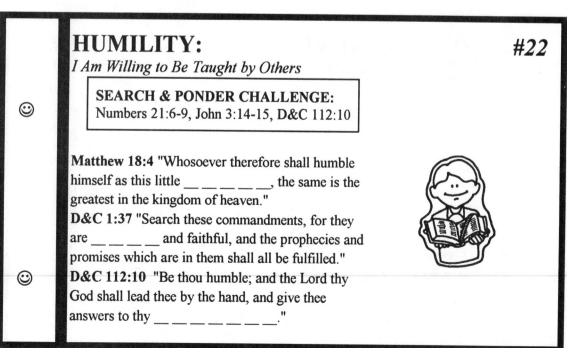

☺

HAPPINESS: #23

I Will Find Happiness as I Follow Jesus

SEARCH & PONDER CHALLENGE:
Read: Joshua 3:13-17, 6:1-5, and 24:15

Joshua 24:15 "Choose you this day whom ye will _ _ _ _ _ _ . . . as for me and my house, we will serve the _ _ _ _."
1 Peter 2:21 "Christ also suffered for us, leaving us an _ _ _ _ _ _ _ _ _, that ye should follow in his _ _ _ _ _ _."

☺

Mosiah 2:41 "Consider on the _ _ _ _ _ _ _ _ _ and happy state of those that keep the commandments of God."

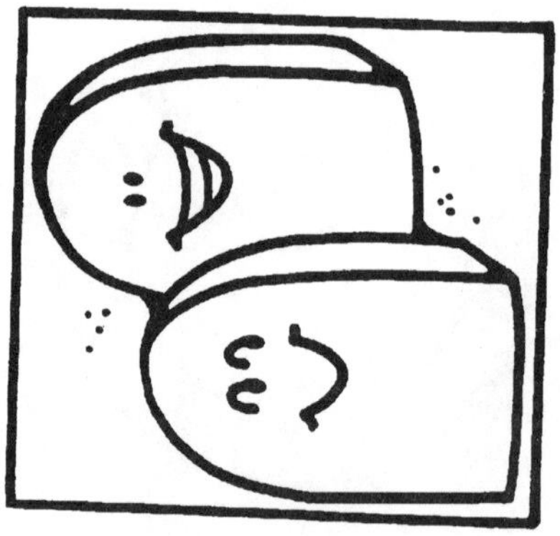

☺

COMMANDMENTS: #24

I Will Trust in the Lord and Obey

SEARCH & PONDER CHALLENGE:
Read Judges 6:12-16 and 7:15-22

1 Nephi 3:7 "I, Nephi, said unto my father: I will _ _ and _ _ the things which the Lord hath commanded, for I know that the Lord _ _ _ _ _ _ _ no commandments unto the children of _ _ _, save he shall

☺

prepare a way for them that they may accomplish the _ _ _ _ _ _ which he commandeth them."

COVENANTS: #25

I Will Develop Spiritual Strength

SEARCH & PONDER CHALLENGE:
Joshua 13:1-5, 24; 15:20; and 16:25-30

Judges 14:5-6 "Samson . . . came to the vinyards of Timnath: and, behold, a young __ __ __ __ __ roared against him. And the __ __ __ __ __ __ __ __ of the Lord came mightily upon him, and he rent him as he would have rent a kid, and he had nothing in his hand."

Judges 15:13-14 "They bound him with two new __ __ __ __ __ __ __ . . . and the spirit of the Lord came mightily upon him . . . and bands [were] loosed."

EXAMPLE: #26

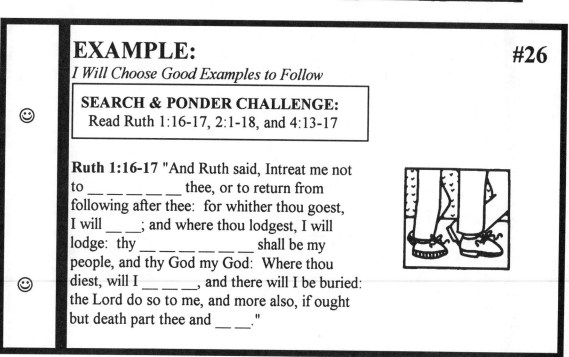

I Will Choose Good Examples to Follow

SEARCH & PONDER CHALLENGE:
Read Ruth 1:16-17, 2:1-18, and 4:13-17

Ruth 1:16-17 "And Ruth said, Intreat me not to __ __ __ __ __ __ thee, or to return from following after thee: for whither thou goest, I will __ __; and where thou lodgest, I will lodge: thy __ __ __ __ __ __ __ shall be my people, and thy God my God: Where thou diest, will I __ __ __, and there will I be buried: the Lord do so to me, and more also, if ought but death part thee and __ __."

☺

☺

HOLY GHOST:

#27

Jesus Christ Speaks to Me Through the Holy Ghost

SEARCH & PONDER CHALLENGE:
Read: 1 Samuel 3:1-10, 19-20

D&C 97:1 "I speak unto you with my _ _ _ _ _ _, even the voice of my _ _ _ _ _ _ _ _, that I may show unto you my will concerning your brethren in the land of Zion, many of whom are truly humble and are _ _ _ _ _ _ _ _ _ _ diligently to learn wisdom and to find _ _ _ _ _ _."

Moroni 10:7 "Ye may know that _ _ is, by the power of the Holy Ghost."

☺

☺

PRAYER:

#28

Heavenly Father Helps Me as I Pray in Faith

SEARCH & PONDER CHALLENGE:
Read: 1 Samuel 17:44-50

1 Samuel 17:37, 45 "David said moreover, The _ _ _ _ _ that delivered me out of the paw of the _ _ _ _ _, and out of the paw of the _ _ _ _ _, he will _ _ _ _ _ _ _ _ _ _ me out of the hand of this Philistine. And Saul said unto David, _ _, and the Lord be with thee . . . . Said David to [Goliath], Thou comest to me with a sword, and with a spear, and with a shield: but I come to thee in the _ _ _ _ _ of the Lord."

FRIENDSHIP: #29

I Can Be a True Friend to Jesus and Others

SEARCH & PONDER CHALLENGE:
Read: 1 Samuel 18:1-4, 20:35-42

1 Samuel 20:42 "And Jonathan said to David, Go in __ __ __ __ __ forasmuch as we have sworn both of us in the name of the __ __ __ __, saying, The Lord be between me and thee, and between my __ __ __ __ and thy seed forever."

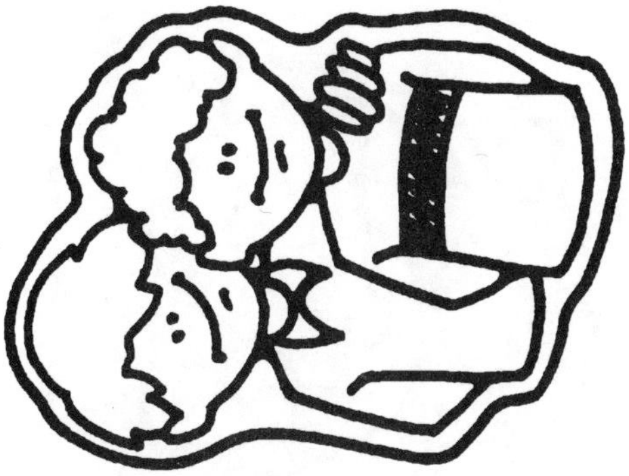

CHOOSE THE RIGHT: #30

I Will Keep My Thoughts and Actions Pure

SEARCH & PONDER CHALLENGE:
Read: 2 Samuel 12:1-7

3 Nephi 14:16-18 "Ye shall know them by their __ __ __ __ __ __ __. Do men gather grapes of thorns, or figs of thistles? Even so every __ __ __ __ tree bringeth forth good fruit; but a corrupt tree bringeth forth __ __ __ __ fruit.
A good tree cannot bring forth evil fruit, neither can a corrupt tree bring forth good fruit. Every tree that bringeth __ __ __ forth good fruit is __ __ __ __ down, and cast into the fire."

WISDOM: #31

I Seek Wisdom, Knowledge, and an Understanding Heart

SEARCH & PONDER CHALLENGE:
Read: 1 Kings 3:5-28

1 Kings 3:11-12, 14 "And God said unto [Solomon], because thou has asked this thing [an understanding heart] . . . I have given thee a wise and an understanding heart . . . And if thou wilt walk in my ways, to keep my . . . commandments . . . I will lengthen thy days."

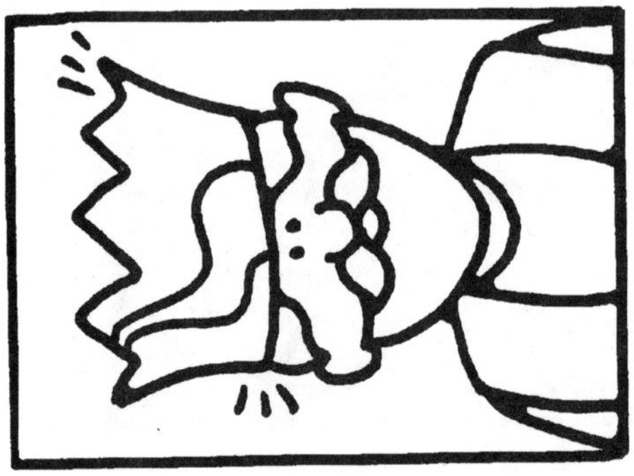

PEER PRESSURE: #32

I Will Be a Positive Influence on My Friends

SEARCH & PONDER CHALLENGE:
Read: 1 Kings 12:1-20

Matthew 4:4 "(Jesus) answered and said, It is written, Man shall not _ _ _ _ _ by _ _ _ _ _ _ _ alone, but by every _ _ _ _ _ that proceedeth out of the mouth of God."
Ephesians 6:1 "Children, _ _ _ _ _ your parents in the _ _ _ _ _: for this is right."
John 13:17 "If ye know these things, _ _ _ _ _ _ are ye if ye do them."

☺

☺

PRIESTHOOD: #33

The Priesthood Blesses My Life

SEARCH & PONDER CHALLENGE:
Read: 1 Kings 17

D&C 121:36 "The rights of the priesthood are inseparably connected with the __ __ __ __ __ __ of heaven."
D&C 127:8-9 "For I am about to restore many things to the earth, pertaining to the priesthood, saith the Lord of Hosts . . . . let all the __ __ __ __ __ __ __ __ be had in order, that they may be put in the archives of my holy temple to be held in remembrance from generation to generation, saith the Lord."

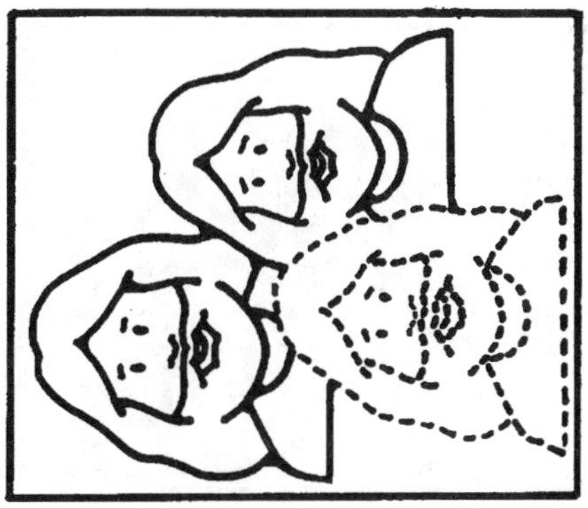

☺

☺

WORSHIP: #34

I Honor Heavenly Father, Jesus Christ and the Holy Ghost

SEARCH & PONDER CHALLENGE:
Read: 1 Kings 18:19-39

1 Kings 18:21 "How long __ __ __ __ ye between __ __ __ opinions? if the Lord be God, follow him."
Exodus 20:3 "Thou shalt have __ __ other gods before me."
Exodus 20:4-5 "Thou shalt not make unto thee any __ __ __ __ __ __ __ image, or any likeness of anything that is in heaven above . . . Thou shalt not bow down thyself to them, nor __ __ __ __ __ them."

OBEDIENCE: #35

I Will Obey Righteous Leaders

SEARCH & PONDER CHALLENGE:
Read: 2 Kings 5:9-14

D&C 21:4-7 "Thou shalt give _ _ _ _ _ unto all his words and commandments which he shall give unto you as he receiveth them, walking in all holiness before me: For his word ye shall receive as if from mine own _ _ _ _ _ _, in all patience and faith. For by doing these things the _ _ _ _ _ _ of hell shall not prevail against you; yea, the Lord God will disperse the . . . darkness . . . and cause the heavens to shake for your good."

SECOND COMING: #36

I Will Prepare by Living Righteously

SEARCH & PONDER CHALLENGE:
Read: Isaiah 54:10, 13-14, 17 and 11:6-9

John 14:27 "Peace I leave with you, my peace I give unto you: not as the _ _ _ _ _ _ giveth, give I unto you. Let not your _ _ _ _ _ _ be troubled, neither let it be afraid."

3 Nephi 27:16 "If he endureth to the _ _ _, behold, him will I hold guiltless before my Father at that day when I shall stand to _ _ _ _ _ _ _ the world."

☺

☺

SCRIPTURES: #37

I Will Be Blessed as I Read the Scriptures and Keep the Commandments

SEARCH & PONDER CHALLENGE:
Read: 2 Kings 23:1-3, 25

2 Chronicles 34:31 "The king . . . made a __ __ __ __ __ __ __ __ before the Lord, to walk after the Lord, and to __ __ __ __ his commandments, and his testimonies, and his statutes, with all his __ __ __ __ __, and with all his soul, to perform the words of the covenant which are written in this __ __ __ __."

☺

☺

FASTING #38

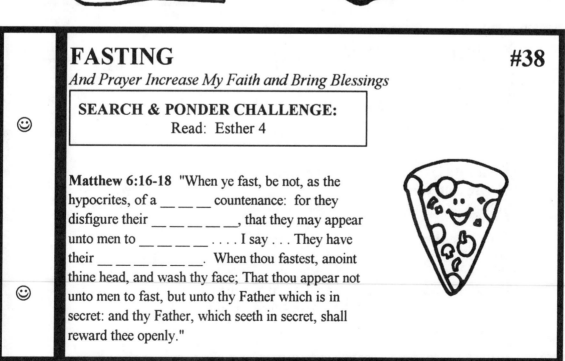

And Prayer Increase My Faith and Bring Blessings

SEARCH & PONDER CHALLENGE:
Read: Esther 4

Matthew 6:16-18 "When ye fast, be not, as the hypocrites, of a __ __ __ countenance: for they disfigure their __ __ __ __ __, that they may appear unto men to __ __ __ __ . . . . I say . . . They have their __ __ __ __ __ __. When thou fastest, anoint thine head, and wash thy face; That thou appear not unto men to fast, but unto thy Father which is in secret: and thy Father, which seeth in secret, shall reward thee openly."

FAITH

#39

Helps Me to Become Strong and Overcome Trials

SEARCH & PONDER CHALLENGE:
Read: Job 27:2-5

Job 27:5-6 "I will not remove mine __ __ __ __ __ __ __ __ __ from me. My righteousness I hold __ __ __ __, and will not let it go: my heart shall not reproach me so long as I live."

Hebrews 11:1 "Now faith is the substance of things __ __ __ __ __ for, the evidence of things not __ __ __ __."

WORD OF WISDOM:

#40

I Will Keep This Law of Health

SEARCH & PONDER CHALLENGE:
Read: Daniel 1:5-17

Daniel 1:5, 8, 15 "The king appointed them a daily provision of the king's __ __ __ __, and of the __ __ __ __ which he drank: so nourishing them three years, that at the end thereof they might stand before the king . . . . Daniel purposed in his heart that he would not defile himself with the portion of the king's meat, nor with the wine which he drank . . . . At the end of ten days their countenances appeared __ __ __ __ __ __."

☺

☺

TESTIMONY: #41

The Gospel of Jesus Christ Is True

SEARCH & PONDER CHALLENGE:
Read: Daniel 3

Alma 53:20 "And they were all young men, and they were exceedingly valiant for __ __ __ __ __ __ __ __, and also for strength and activity; but behold, this was not all—they were men who were __ __ __ __ at all times in whatsoever thing they were entrusted."

Daniel 3:12 "They serve not thy gods, nor worship the golden __ __ __ __ __ which thou hast set up."

☺

☺

PRAYER: #42

I Will Pray Morning and Night

SEARCH & PONDER CHALLENGE:
Read: Daniel 6:16-23

Daniel 6:21-23 "Then said Daniel unto the king, O king, __ __ __ __ for ever. My God hath sent his __ __ __ __ __, and hath shut the lions' mouths, that they have not hurt me: forasmuch as before him innocency was found in me; and also before thee, O king, have I done no __ __ __ __. Then was the king exceeding glad for him . . . no manner of hurt was found upon him, because he __ __ __ __ __ __ __ __ __ in his God."

☺

☺

REPENTANCE:

#43

Heavenly Father Forgives All Who Truly Repent

SEARCH & PONDER CHALLENGE:
Jonah 1:1-3, 11-17; 2:1-2; and 3:3-5, 10

Jonah 2:9-10 "I [Jonah] will sacrifice unto thee with the voice of thanksgiving; I will __ __ __ that that I have vowed. Salvation is of the __ __ __ __. And the Lord spake unto the fish, and it vomited out Jonah upon the __ __ __ land."

☺

☺

TITHING:

#44

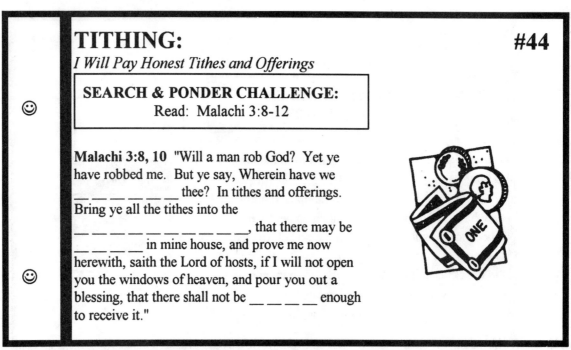

I Will Pay Honest Tithes and Offerings

SEARCH & PONDER CHALLENGE:
Read: Malachi 3:8-12

Malachi 3:8, 10 "Will a man rob God? Yet ye have robbed me. But ye say, Wherein have we __ __ __ __ __ __ __ thee? In tithes and offerings. Bring ye all the tithes into the __ __ __ __ __ __ __ __ __ __ __ __, that there may be __ __ __ __ in mine house, and prove me now herewith, saith the Lord of hosts, if I will not open you the windows of heaven, and pour you out a blessing, that there shall not be __ __ __ __ __ enough to receive it."